COLLECTING, CULTURING, AND CARING FOR LIVING MATERIALS: A GUIDE FOR THE TEACHER, STUDENT AND HOBBYIST

Includes Directions for Construction of Inexpensive Equipment

By William E. Claflin

Illustrations by David Claflin

COLLECTING, CULTURING, AND CARING FOR LIVING MATERIALS:
A GUIDE FOR TEACHER, STUDENT AND HOBBYIST

By William E. Claflin

CENTURY TWENTY ONE PUBLISHING

PUBLISHED BY

**CENTURY TWENTY ONE PUBLISHING
POST OFFICE BOX 8
SARATOGA, CALIFORNIA 95070**

LIBRARY OF CONGRESS CARD CATALOG NUMBER

80-69329

I.S.B.N.

0-86548-026-5

TABLE OF CONTENTS

		Page
I.	PREFACE	1
II.	CARE OF LIVING MATERIALS	5
	ANIMALS	5
	Ants	5
	Aphids	8
	Brine Shrimp	11
	Butterflies and Moths	15
	Chameleons, Fence Lizards and Other Native Lizards	19
	Cockroaches and Crickets	21
	Crayfish	23
	Damselflies and Damselfly Nymphs	27
	Daphnia (Water Fleas)	30
	Frogs, Toads, and Salamanders	34
	Fruit Fly	39
	Guppies	42
	Hermit Crab	44
	Isopods (Sowbugs: Pillbugs)	46
	Mealworm	48
	Praying Mantises	51
	Snails (Pond and Land)	53
	PLANTS	55
	Algae	56
	Anacharis (Elodea)	58
	Fern	60
	Moss	62
	Sagittaria (Arrowhead)	64
	Vallisneria (Eelgrass or Water Celery)	66
	Wolffia (Duckweed)	68
III.	EQUIPMENT IDEAS	69
	Fruit Fly Transfer Chamber	70
	Germination Tray	71
	Homemade Balance	72
	Light Table	73
	Mealworm Habitat	75
	Plastic Scoop/Funnel	76

iii

TABLE OF CONTENTS (Continued)

Page

Runway to Determine Optimum Temperature
    Range for Isopods   77
Single Snail Habitat   78
Terrarium   79
Throw Away Aquarium or Terrarium   80

ANNOTATED REFERENCES   82

REFERENCES   83

APPENDICES   87

    Appendix A   Biological Hazard   88
    Appendix B   Biological Suppliers   89
    Appendix C   Comparison of American and
                 Metric Units of Measurement   90
    Appendix D   Living Materials Food Chart   91
    Appendix E   Temporary Care for New Animal
                 Arrivals   93
    Appendix F   Temporary Care for New Plant
                 Arrivals   95

PREFACE

As an encouragement to those science teachers who use
live materials with their students, a statement by the late
Margaret Mead at a convention of the National Science Teachers Association is most appropriate: ". . . we must
introduce children to living things and not just dead dogfish
or whatever, or pictures of dead dogfish, or diagrams of dead
dogfish!"[1] As science teachers and parents we can provide
students with the opportunity to observe living materials
and their interactions within many environments.

Teachers and parents also observe that experiences with
living materials motivate students to observe, ask questions,
and engage in higher learning processes.

The original purpose of this guide was to assist
teachers who inquired about and asked for assistance in
obtaining and maintaining living materials in their classrooms. From my own experience teaching in elementary and
secondary classrooms and in preservice and inservice science
methods classes at Fort Hays State University, I have faced
the problems and frustrations of working with living materials
in the classroom. I have provided directions and information
in response to personal inquiries from many teachers, through
class instruction, and through demonstrations in workshops

---

[1]Margaret Mead, "Creating a Scientific Climate for
Children," Science and Children, (May, 1977) Vol. 14, No. 8.,
pp. 11-12.

1

over the years at Kansas Association of Science Teachers (KATS) camps and at conventions.

In my experience answers to common inquiries teachers, parents, and students make about maintaining living materials are not available in a common source. Hence, this guide was organized to provide the common name of the animal or plant, classification as to phylum and class, a brief definition of each classification group, collection areas and equipment, classroom habitats, feeding and watering, and sexing, breeding, and hatching information. Teachers, students and parents can easily find information about the topics by referring to the name of the animal or plant in the table of contents and turning to that page. The scientific names are given to assist students in further research in reference materials.

Through my experiences it became obvious that information on maintenance of living materials and techniques for construction of inexpensive equipment for that purpose would be valuable to parents interested in encouraging creative and inquisitive children and to those creative, inquisitive students (of all ages) themselves. Parents may need such a guide to provide information on habitats and feeding for curious children who bring home an unannounced frog or butterfly or who may want to buy a chameleon at the pet store.

Seldom has adequate equipment been readily available to me in my teaching situations. Therefore, it has been necessary to build or improvise my own equipment. By making inexpensive items with disposable cartons, etc., (1) the cost is kept low, (2) storage is minimized, and (3) students have more opportunities for hands-on experiences. Since each student or small group can have individualized equipment, comparisons among various projects, e.g. aquaria, provide opportunities to observe interactions.

This guide provides suggestions for collecting, culturing, and caring for selected animals and plants that are used in the Science Curriculum Improvement Study (SCIS), Elementary Science Study (ESS), People-Concepts-Processes (PCP), Modular Approach to Elementary Science (MAPS) and other textbooks commonly used in current elementary and science classrooms. These selections include animals and plants about which teachers in my geographical area have asked questions over the years.

The animals included in this section were selected to demonstrate food chains, growth patterns, life cycles, and visibility of life processes. The information provided extends beyond that provided in the guides and textbooks relative to the selected animals.

Since many of the animals included here are difficult to find in off-season or in certain locations, a list of suppliers is provided in the Appendix.

To the many teachers who have provided suggestions, especially those of the Kansas Association of Teachers of Science, to my own students who tried them, and to my colleagues at Fort Hays State University in various science fields who provided references and information, I extend my thanks.

Animal: ANTS

Phylum: Arthropoda (Terrestrial, aerial and aquatic
          forms; segmented bodies and chitenous exo-
          skeletons)

Class: Insecta (Head, thorax and abdomen; six legs;
          one pair of antennae)

A. Collecting Areas and Equipment

   1. Ants can be found anywhere in buildings, parks,
       fields, etc., throughout the United States.
       Early spring is the best time to start looking
       for ant hills in pastures, etc.

   2. Ants can be collected by digging, trapping, or
       purchasing. Dig in a 6 to 12 inch radius
       around the ant hill opening and 12 to 18 inches
       deep to collect your eggs, larvae, pupae, and
       hopefully a queen. Collect about 50 or so to
       start the new colony. Place this dirt in an
       escape proof container for transportation. Note:
       Be sure air is available for the animals and that
       the dirt is damp. A second technique that can
       be used to trap ants is to place a sugar-water
       soaked paper towel or a sweet object in a
       darkened ice cream container near the ant hill.

   3. A tile spade would be the best instrument to
       use for digging. Note: Be sure to fill the
       hole back with dirt so that the remainder of
       the animals can reform their colony.

   4. Place the ants in a cold environment such as a
       styrofoam chest for one or two hours; this
       will allow you to transfer them to other con-
       tainers more easily.

B. Classroom Habitats

   1. Ant houses can be purchased from pet stores and
       biological suppliers. However, inexpensive ant
       houses can be prepared by placing two pieces of
       glass (12" x 18" or any reasonable size) side by
       side and one to two centimeters apart. The two
       pieces of glass can be held apart with wood,

plastic or metal materials approximately two
centimeters by the length and width of your
glass. Glue or use some type of tape (Duct
tape is excellent) for holding the glass
together. The top spacer should have three
or four holes drilled through it so that
water and air can enter the container. One
hole should have a plastic straw through it
that goes to the bottom of the soil so that
water can be added, and the other holes should
be covered with a very fine mesh wire or
cloth. The top of the soil should be kept dry.
Note: <u>Be sure to plug the straw so that the
ants don't escape.</u> Also, an opening needs to
be left for placing some types of food materials in the container. Many other ideas for
housing can be found in magazines and books
listed in the references in this guide.

C. Feeding and Watering

1. Feed ants very small pieces of carrot, potato,
   bread, fruits, etc. Note: <u>Be sure not to
   place more food in the container than they
   will eat.</u> (Place only a very few pieces in the
   container at a time). <u>Should they not eat this
   in a reasonable time, or if it starts to mold,
   remove it.</u>

2. Keep the soil moist by pouring water down the
   plastic straw and allowing the water to soak
   up through the soil from bottom to within one
   inch of the top. Note: <u>Be sure the soil is
   kept moist.</u>

D. Sexing, Breeding and Hatching

1. Three types of ants--workers, males, and queens--
   can usually be found in each colony in the
   natural habitat. The queen will be the largest
   of the three. The queen will grow wings for a
   mating flight in the late spring or early fall.
   These wings will break off or be bit off right
   after the flight. The queen's thorax or mid-
   section will be noticeably large right after
   her mating flight because of the wing muscle
   development. The male and worker (female, unmated,
   and wingless) will usually be smaller in size.
   The male will not work and cannot feed itself.

Therefore, after the mating flight the males will normally fall to the ground and die. Worker ants will provide food and special care for the eggs.

2. The queen ants may mate with a male from her own colony or from a different colony. Queens and workers are females coming from fertilized eggs. Males are from unfertilized eggs.

3. The queen ant will find a location for a nest very soon after landing from the mating flight; this may be her own colony, a different ant colony, or she may establish a new nest. The queen will drop her wings and start laying eggs. The ant goes through complete metamorphosis, i.e., egg, larva, pupa, and adult stages. The egg stage will last about 24 days, the larval stage from 30 to 71 days, and the pupal stage about 20 days. Approximately 3 months will pass from egg to adult stage.

Animal: APHIDS

Phylum: Arthropoda (Terrestrial, aerial and aquatic
          forms; segmented bodies and chitenous exo-
          skeleton)

Class: Insecta (Head, thorax, and abdomen; six legs;
          one pair of antennae)

A. Collecting Area and Equipment

   1. In the spring aphids can sometimes be found on
       the foliage of climbing roses, peach trees,
       shrubs, and other vegetation. Later in the
       summer aphids can also be found on milo or
       other grain sorghum plants or the larvae can
       be found on the roots of corn plants. Aphids
       can be purchased from one of the biological
       suppliers listed in Appendix B.

   2. These animals can best be collected by using
       a soft bristled brush to transfer them from
       a source plant to a plant in a transporting
       container. The container for transporting
       them could be a clear plastic juice cup which
       has a small pea plant growing in it. Place
       the aphids on the pea plant and cover with a
       second clear plastic juice cup which has
       small holes burned in the bottom of cup with
       a paper clip held over a candle. Tape the
       two cups together with masking tape. See the
       individual snail habitat shown in this guide
       on page 78.

B. Classroon Habitat

   1. A habitat for aphids can be made from any type
       of container, terrarium, or aquarium that will
       allow students to observe aphids, provide high
       humidity, allow adequate light for plant growth,
       and be water proof. The container should be
       filled with two or three inches of soil, and
       pea seeds should be planted according to direc-
       tions on the package. Pea seeds should be at
       the seedling stage before transferring aphids
       to the new habitat.

2. Normal room temperature will be adequate for growth and reproduction.

3. Cover the container with a lid or a sheet of clear plastic so the humidity can be kept high (around 60%). An open jar of water set in a corner of the terrarium will help maintain the humidity level. Note: <u>Be sure to leave an air opening.</u>

C. Feeding and Watering

1. Aphids require pea seedling plants to feed on; therefore, you will need to plant new seeds at least once a week so that a continuous source of pea seedlings will be available for food. Note: If the new plants are nearby the old plants, the aphids will crawl to them. <u>If not, you will need to transfer the aphids with a soft bristled brush.</u>

2. The only watering necessary is to keep the plants in a healthy state and to maintain a high humidity. Aphids feed on plant juices.

D. Sexing, Breeding, Birth, and Hatching

1. During late September winged males and females are produced and are usually found on the trunks of trees. The male will always have wings and be smaller than the female. In the spring and summer you can usually find only females, and they will be either wingless or winged.

2. In the fall the winged females will produce a generation of wingless females by parthenogensis, and it is these females that the winged males mate with to produce eggs for the next spring.

3. The eggs produced in fall are large and have a thick black protective shell. These eggs will lie dormant in tree bark crevices unharmed by water throughout the winter. Warm spring weather will cause the eggs to hatch, producing only wingless females. The

wingless females will reach maturity in about
ten days and continue to produce, by live
birth, generations of winged and wingless
females all summer--sometimes a dozen generations.

4. As the nymphs mature to adults they will molt
    several times. The discarded skins are white
    and can be easily seen on the plant and soil
    surface surrounding the pea seedling.

Animal: BRINE SHRIMP

Phylum: Arthropoda (Terrestrial, aerial and aquatic
         forms; segmented bodies and chitenous exo-
         skeletons)

Class: Crustacea (Crust-like shell formed by
         hardened calcareous deposits)

A. Collecting Area and Equipment

    1. Brine shrimp are found only in salt water areas
        (except oceans). Brine shrimp can be dipped
        from shallow salt water pools near salt flats,
        salt lakes, etc. Since many teachers would not
        have these areas available, they would need to
        purchase the eggs at a pet store or biological
        supply house. See Appendix B.

    2. Eggs which have been collected need to be
        dried and stored in a cool place. Also, pur-
        chased eggs should be kept dry and stored in
        a cool place.

B. Classroom Habitats (Aquariums)

    1. Fish aquaria, clear plastic cups, plastic
        shoe or sweater boxes, plastic lined shoe
        boxes, milk cartons cut in half, glass cake
        baking dishes, etc. make good classroom con-
        tainers. Be careful of glass containers
        around younger children. Metal containers
        should not be used.

    2. Salt water solutions prepared for the above
        containers should be about one tablespoon of
        salt per cup of water. However, students may
        want to vary these amounts for some eggs. Be
        sure the water is aged (sets 72 hours or more)
        tap water, well water, spring water, or
        strained pond water. The salt used should be
        non-iodized, rock salt, or marine salt. Again,
        students may want to try iodized table salt to
        observe the effect.

3. Be sure the water level is marked and that water is added to keep it at this level during the hatching and growing period. (Note: Aged, well, pond or spring water, not salt water, should be added. See above.)

4. Be sure that aquaria are not placed in direct sunlight. However, an optimum temperature range of somewhere between 70°F to 85°F should be maintained.

5. To enhance the development of brine shrimp, bubble air through the water with either an aerator or a household baster one or two times a day.

C. Feeding and Watering

1. Dried baker's yeast bought at the grocery store can be used as food. Be sure that only a small pinch is used at each feeding. Don't overfeed. Should too much yeast be put on the water, use a paper towel to soak off some of it. Also, brine shrimp feed on algae and other microorganisms which can be added.

2. Be sure to keep the water level the same as suggested in Part B.

3. Feeding once or twice a day will be enough.

4. If you are overfeeding, a scum will probably form on top of the water. Remove as much as possible of this with a baster or paper towel.

D. Breeding and Hatching

1. Optimum conditions will allow the brine shrimp to mature in about six weeks and begin mating at this time. Usually mating occurs after the female has molted. Females can be observed as having lateral egg pouches. Males will have large appendages up by the head which are used for mating.

2. Optimum temperatures for hatching would be normal room temperature--72° to 75°F.

3. Caution the children against spreading too many eggs on the water for hatching. Overcrowding should always be prevented.

4. Be sure the hatching container is not disturbed; the eggs should stay in the water.

5. When batches of eggs are laid by the females and seen floating on the surface of the water, they will need to be removed and thoroughly dried before they will hatch again. (If you aren't going to use them soon, be sure to store in a cool, dry place.)

Brine Shrimp

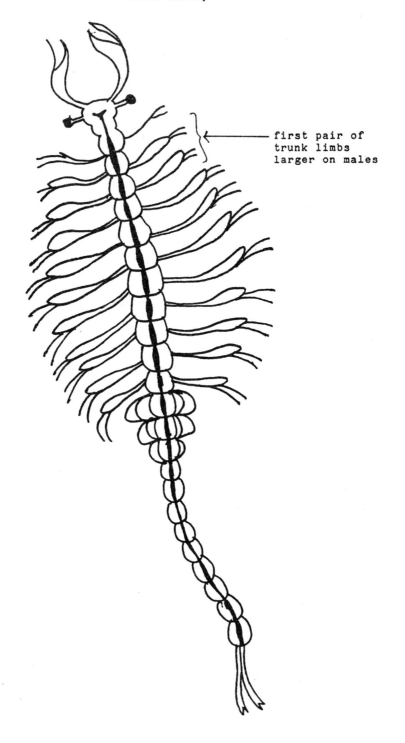

first pair of
trunk limbs
larger on males

Animals: BUTTERFLIES AND MOTHS

Phylum: Arthropoda (Terrestrial, aerial and aquatic
forms; segmented bodies and chitenous. exoskeleton)

Class: Insecta (Head, thorax and abdomen; six legs;
one pair of antennae)

A. Collecting Areas and Equipment

    1. Butterflies and moths are common to every
state; however, some are so rare that they
can only be found in certain isolated areas
such as on mountain tops. Moths will be out
at night and will outnumber butterflies by a
10 to 1 count. Butterflies appear more
numerous because they are more active during
the daylight and are more conspicuously
colored. Butterflies and moths can be found
in fields, on shrubs, trees and on some
household fabrics.

    2. You are most likely to find cocoons or
chrysalis in the late fall or early spring
on fences or houses, bushes, branches, between barkridges, and in sheltered areas.
One can pick up the larvae of either the
moth or butterfly. In the pupal stage, one
can pick off twigs with a chrysalis or
cocoon attached. Adult butterflies and moths
can be caught with a net.

    3. Be sure to transport them in containers that
allow for total wing spread and provide protection from damage to the wings. (Wire containers could be dangerous to the wings during
transporting.) Habitat materials most nearly
like those on which they are found should be
collected. Note: <u>Be sure you keep their areas
moist but not over watered.</u>

B. Classroom Habitats

    1. Butterflies and moths are easy to rear if you keep them in clean, airy cages. The cages can be made from cardboard boxes with the sides cut out and nylon netting placed over the openings. Also, a circular cage can be made from screen wire and two pie pans. Lace the screen wire together and connect the bottom and top pans with wire ties or hooks. A metal or plastic container will need to be placed at the bottom of the cardboard container. Dirt should be placed in the bottom trays for growing plants to provide moisture for those moths that pupate underground. Twigs and plants should be placed in the cages to provide places for the butterflies to place their chrysalis and moths to hang their cocoons and/or to climb up to shake out their soft new wings. Note: Be sure to keep soil moist during the pupating period.

C. Feeding and Watering

    1. Butterflies and moths will be found on fences, houses, bushes, shrubs, garden and field plants and trees. Collect some of the food on which the larvae or adult is feeding when captured. Most caterpillars are very specific in their diet, many feeding on only one kind of plant. All butterflies are herbivorous. Don't allow moldy food to stay in their habitats. Moisture will come from the mist on the plant leaves and the juices extracted from stems and leaves. No open water trays are needed or should be placed in their cages.

D. Sexing, Breeding and Hatching

    1. The two sexes of butterflies and moths are quite different in appearance, often so much so that no one would suspect them of belonging to the same species. In some moths these sex differences extend beyond color and size, the males being winged while the females are without wings. Butterfly Example: The female Swallow-tail can be recognized by the bluish area on the hindwings above the tail. Moth Example: The Evergreen Bagworm Moths are very unattractive insects. Females are wingless, legless

and worm-like. Males have transparent wings as a result of loss of their scales soon after emerging from their larval homes.

2. When the adult stage of the butterfly and moth is reached, the primary concern of the adults is to mate and lay eggs. Males find their mates by sight or scent. All female butterflies and moths that are ready to breed give off a scent that attracts the male from several feet away to several miles away. Once in the area the male then secretes a scent which stimulates the mating process. However, it is thought that more butterflies mate by sight and moths by scent, because butterflies are more active by day and moths by night.

3. Butterflies and moths differ in their egg laying habits in that moth eggs are usually laid in clusters and coated with scales, hair, or a tough secretion, and butterfly eggs are more likely to be found singly or in groups arranged on the surface of leaves or stems without any special protection. They deposit the egg on the plant which is to be the food of the young. Most butterfly and moth eggs will hatch and become caterpillars within one to two weeks after they are laid. As soon as the caterpillar emerges from its egg case it may be observed eating the egg case. Then it will feed ravenously on nearby plant materials. Molting may be observed. The pupal stage (chrysalis or cocoon) will follow. Generally this is over the winter. Many of the egg cases and larvae can be found in the fall and may be allowed to emerge in the classroom during the winter if appropriate temperature and moisture are maintained. Since specific food may not be available, it will be very difficult to keep the adult moths and butterflies alive. It is preferable to bring a cocoon or chrysalis inside to develop when plant materials are likely to be available.

Stages of Development of a Butterfly

Stages

1) Egg
2) Larva
3) Pupa
4) Adult

Animals: CHAMELEONS, FENCE LIZARDS AND OTHER NATIVE
           LIZARDS

Phylum: Chordata (Dorsal nerve cord; gill slits--
           temporary or permanent; never more than four
           legs)

Class: Reptilia (Terrestrial or semiaquatic; breathe
           by lungs in all stages; scales; cold-blooded)

A. Collecting Area and Equipment

    1. Lizards and chameleons can be found mainly in
        the lower half of the United States and
        especially in the semitropical region of
        Southeastern United States. Fence lizards are
        much more wide spread than chameleons.

    2. Collecting equipment: To capture use a long
        handled net with a fine mesh bag; round ice
        cream carton or plastic container may be used
        for transporting. Be sure to use some type
        of procedure to keep this animal warm if it
        is to be transported during the winter.

    3. Don't handle these animals by their tail.
        Place the hand around the body.

B. Classroom Habitats (Terraria)

    1. Each of the following habitats should be
        irradiated with ultraviolet light for about
        10 minutes each day. This will prolong the
        life of the animal.

    2. Temperature of 70°-80° should be maintained
        for the animals.

    3. Glass or plastic gallon jars, aquaria, and
        cardboard boxes which are plastic lined can
        be used to house these animals. Avoid the
        use of metal cages that can injure the feet
        or nose areas.

    4. Each of the above should have a plant(s) or
        dead branches for climbing on.

5. The bottom of the container should be covered with dry sand.

6. Be sure all habitats have a tight fitting cover that is porous so that the humidity doesn't become too high.

C. Feeding and Watering

1. Soft bodied insects are the best source of food for chameleons and lizards. Examples: flies, mealworms, isopods, crickets, and moths. The first three animals above are very easy to culture in the classroom. If you use fruit flies, place a container (vial with a small hole in the cap so that fruit flies can get in and out for food and to lay eggs) in the cage. Replace with a new container of fruit flies after the medium dries out or the population gets small. Also, you could and should vary their food by placing a few mealworms and isopods in from time to time. Note of Caution: Mealworms or insects with heavy chitinous exoskeletons can be injurious to some lizards if used as a steady food. Living food is desired by most lizards.

2. Water these animals by spraying the walls and plants once or twice a day with a clean spray bottle of water. Also, spraying their bodies will aid them when shedding their skins. Note of Caution: Chameleons can't drink from a dish.

D. Breeding and Hatching

1. Lizards rarely breed in a classroom habitat. However, should you find lizard eggs and want to try hatching them--place them on a damp paper towel (not wet) and place them in a bread wrapper which you seal tightly at the open end and leave at normal room temperature. Chameleons usually lay two or three eggs which will hatch in about six weeks. A horned lizard may lay up to 30 eggs; in other lizards up to a dozen young may be born alive. Some species will hatch their eggs in a few hours and others take up to several weeks.

Animals: COCKROACHES AND CRICKETS

Phylum: Arthropoda (Terrestrial, aerial and aquatic
           forms; segmented bodies and chitenous exo-
           skeletons)

Class: Insecta (Head, thorax, and abdomen; six legs;
           one pair of antennae)

A. Collecting Areas and Equipment

    1. Crickets and cockroaches of different species
        are widely distributed over the United States.
        They can be found under rocks in moist places,
        in fields, barns, homes, stores, etc. Also,
        various quantities of both sexes can be
        purchased from a biological supplier.

    2. These animals can best be trapped by placing
        a funnel (the funnel could be made from small
        mesh, wire, etc.) in a hole in a wooden box.
        Place some type of food (raw meat) in the
        containers. Also, many species can be captured
        by hand or by nets from under rocks. Note: Be
        sure to cool them for 10 to 20 minutes before
        transferring to a new habitat! This makes them
        less active for moving.

B. Classroom Habitats

    1. All types of large glass, galvanized and plastic
        containers can be used for housing these animals.

    2. The habitat should be fitted with a tight cover
        that allows for circulation of air but is
        escape proof. The habitat should be placed
        out of direct sunlight, have several objects
        for the animals to crawl on and hide under and
        have soil that is moist in part of the area
        for egg laying. The soil should be replaced
        every few months if you plan to keep the
        animals over an extended time.

    3. The habitat should be placed in an area which
        has a 70° to 90° temperature.

    4. Don't let mold form in the habitat.

5. The humidity should be kept around 60%; an open container of water or moist paper towels can help provide this level.

C. Feeding and Watering

1. Dry dog food, celery, potato, apple, pieces of cheese, fried egg, stale bread, etc. can be fed to these animals. Note: High protein foods are needed to keep them from eating on each other. Also, don't allow the food to get moldy. Place the food away from the area that you water most and where a watering device is located.

2. Water needs to be available at all times (No open container). Use a cotton or guaze plugged test tube type watering container. (Olive jars are excellent. Fill jar with water, plug tightly, lay jar on side.)

D. Sexing, Breeding, and Hatching

1. Female crickets can be identified by the long ovipositor on the rear of the body. Male crickets can be recognized by the chirping sound made by rubbing their wings together.

2. European house crickets may breed at any time, so all stages may be found at any time during a year. Other crickets will have specific breeding times during a calendar year. Breeding in other species may take place in a very short period of time or over several months.

3. All types of reproduction in crickets and roaches are represented by stages of incomplete metamorphosis. The egg will hatch in some species in one to three weeks, depending on the temperature of the soil. The total maturation process from nymph to adult may take from several weeks in some species to several months in others.

Animal: CRAYFISH

Phylum: Arthropoda (Terrestrial, aerial and aquatic forms; segmented bodies and chitenous exo-skeletons)

Class: Crustacea (Crust-like shell formed by hardened calcareous deposits)

A. Collecting Area and Equipment

    1. Crayfish can be found in quiet waters of streams, rivers, ponds, lakes, and marshes throughout the United States. They will usually be hiding under rocks, wood, debris or in burrows in the stream banks, etc. Since they feed mainly at night, you will need to move objects in the streams very slowly to expose them.

    2. They can be caught by hand by approaching them from the rear and grasping the carapace. Note: <u>You need to be very quick and press down on them firmly to get a good grasp before lifting</u>. Dip nets, traps, and scoops made from plastic containers (Scoop is illustrated in the guide) may be used.

B. Classroom Habitats

    1. Containers for housing crayfish could be large aquaria (10 gallons or more), a plastic wading pool, or large boxes lined with plastic. The bottom needs to be covered with two inches of gravel, and sides need to be protected by thin pieces of wood so the crayfish cannot poke holes in the plastic. An illustration of how to line a box is found in the guide, p. 81.

    2. Be sure to place the habitat in some location out of direct sunlight or extreme heat. Normal room temperature, 68° to 72°, is adequate.

    3. Place large rocks which stick up out of the water at several locations in the habitat so that crayfish can climb on them and hide under them.

4. Use well, spring, pond, or aged tap water for filling the containers. Allow the water which the animal has been collected in to reach the same temperature as the container water. Suspend a plastic bag or gallon jar containing collected water and the animal in the new habitat until temperatures are the same. Then float the animal into the new habitat. Note: <u>Sudden temperature changes can be harmful.</u> Water should only be about one to two inches above the gravel and should be changed two or three times a week if you are not using an aerator. Note: <u>Water level and changing are critical for oxygen needs of these animals.</u> Make sure water level is kept at a constant height.

5. Oxygen can and should be provided by an aerator for a large number of animals. Oxygen will be adequate for one or two animals if you maintain the 1-2 inches water level so crayfish can obtain oxygen near the surface. However, you can supplement the amount of oxygen by bubbling air from a household baster in the water two or three times a day.

6. Be sure no toxic substances such as detergents, etc. are used to clean the container before it is used.

7. Many types of containers (not metal) can be used to make homes for these animals. Plastic or clay flower pots with portions of the rim broken away are excellent hiding areas. If there are holes in the bottoms of the pots, cover them with foil to darken.

8. Be sure the water does not become foul due to feeding, death, or other reasons.

C. Feeding and Watering

1. Crayfish will eat easily raised animals or animal parts, such as meal worms, small pieces of liver, insect larvae, earthworms, etc. Any type of frozen fish or meats can be used for food. Note: <u>They should only be fed small amounts of food twice a week and should be fed in a separate container</u>

other than the water in which they live.
This will keep their habitat water from
becoming polluted. Also, be sure the
water in the feeding container is approximately the same temperature and depth.

2. Students can observe the feeding if you
    will place the crayfish in a plastic shoe
    box or other clear container so the
    students can observe from the bottom.
    (Crayfish mouth parts are located on the
    ventral surface of the body.)

    Be sure the water level is kept at about
    one to two inches in depth. Refill to
    that level each day or so with water
    (aged, well, spring, filtered pond, etc.)
    of the same temperature as the habitat.

D. Sexing, Breeding and Hatching

1. The sex of a crayfish can be determined by
    observing the size of the first set of
    appendages (swimmerets) on the tail. The first
    male appendage will be quite large and sturdy
    looking when compared to others on the tail.
    Female swimmerets will all look the same,
    larger than the male, and fuzzier than the
    male.

2. Female crayfish will become fertile by the
    end of the summer and will mate during the
    fall or winter. During mating the male will
    deposit sperm around the oviduct opening on
    the outside of the female body. This may
    take several minutes to several hours. During
    the egg laying period the sperm will fertilize
    the eggs as they come from the oviduct. There
    may be several hundred eggs laid during the
    spring which will take from two to twenty days
    to hatch. The young will remain attached to
    the mother's swimmerets for several weeks.

    Note: If you move or handle a female carrying
    eggs, she might start eating the eggs. Also,
    always remove dead animals or eggs floating
    on the surface to avoid polluting the water.

Crayfish (male)

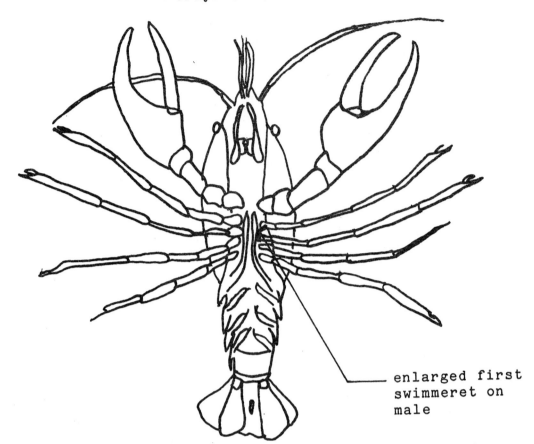

enlarged first
swimmeret on
male

Animal: DAMSELFLIES AND DAMSELFLY NYMPHS

Phylum: Arthropoda (Terrestrial, aerial and aquatic
forms; segmented bodies and chitenous exo-
skeletons)

Class: Insecta (Head, thorax, and abdomen; six legs;
one pair of antennae)

A. Collecting Areas and Equipment

   1. Some species of this exquisite insect can
      be found in the United States from Florida and
      Texas north to the shores of the Great Lakes
      and into Canada. Ponds, ditches, and canals
      with thick areas of vegetation are their
      favorite habitat. Damselflies are very weak
      in flying; therefore, they are not usually found
      very far from their birthplace.

   2. It is best to observe the behavior of damsel-
      flies in flight, feeding and egg laying before
      you start to collect them. A long handled in-
      sect net which has a very deep cone should be
      used to catch the damselfly. Hint: When you
      have scooped the damselfly from the air or from
      a reed with your net, twist your wrist quickly
      so that the bag flips over the wire. Also,
      damselfly nymphs can be found clinging to under-
      water stems; therefore, collecting bottom
      vegetation in an area of high adult population
      should give you a number of nymphs for an
      aquarium. A plastic scoop or large mouth plas-
      tic jar could be used to scoop water plants
      found near the bottom which would have nymphs
      clinging to them. Note: Transport the adult
      in a container which has enough room so that the
      adult doesn't damage its wings.

B. Classroom Habitats

   1. Any type aquarium would make an adequate con-
      tainer for the damselfly. Water plants from
      the collection area or those bought at pet shops

can be added to the aquarium for the nymphs to
cling to while maturing. Add pond, spring,
well or aged tap water to replace evaporated
water. Place a fine nylon net over the aquarium
should nymphs reach the adult stage. The very
fine mesh net will be needed to keep fruit flies
or other small flying insects in the aquarium
for food.

C. Feeding and Watering

1. An adult damselfly feeds mainly on soft-bodied
    insects such as gnats, midges, mosquitoes,
    fruit flies, etc. and the nymphs feed mainly on
    fresh water animals such as mosquito larva,
    daphnia, cyclops, etc. Fruit flies are easy to
    culture and can be released in the aquarium each
    day for adult food.

2. Since the egg is laid in water and the nymph
    spends its entire life in the water, be sure
    the aquarium has adequate water for the plant
    and animal populations at all times. Keep the
    evaporated water replaced with pond, well,
    spring, or aged tap water.

D. Sexing, Breeding and Hatching

1. Damselfly sex, in some species, can be recog-
    nized by the color of wings; that is, the
    males wings of some species are black and the
    female's wings are pale with white spots. Also,
    the male has a shiny white spot at the top of
    his abdomen which he displays to attract a mating
    partner.

2. Damselflies mate during the early spring or sum-
    mer. Some species mate more than once during
    the summer; therefore, it is possible to have
    several populations of damselfly nymphs during
    a season. After a short courtship, the male
    seizes a female with his tail appendages and
    flies with her to rest on a plant. The sperm is
    passed from the male to the female and the eggs
    are fertilized at this time. The female will
    then submerge her body, either partly or com-
    pletely, to deposit the eggs on or in the stems of
    submerged plants. During this time the male will
    continue to hover close by, ready to attack any
    possible intruders.

3. Hatching time varies with the climate and water conditions, but it usually takes the eggs from twenty-six to twenty-nine days to hatch. The nymphal life of the damselfly might extent for up to two or three years, but the adult life is comparatively short, usually about four weeks.

Animal: DAPHNIA (WATER-FLEAS)

Phylum: Arthropoda (Terrestrial, aerial and aquatic
           forms; segmented bodies and chitenous exo-
           skeletons)

Class: Crustacea (Crust-like shell formed by hardened
           calcareous deposits)

A. Collecting Area and Equipment

    1. Daphnia are widely distributed throughout the
        United States in both fresh water and marine
        habitats. Daphnia can be found in shallow
        and calm water areas such as lakes, ponds,
        streams, cattle tanks, etc. Presence of non-
        filamentous algae and bacteria provide
        excellent conditions for abundant numbers
        of Daphnia. Water areas which receive run
        off from farm animal wastes are usually
        habitats that have large numbers of Daphnia.

    2. Daphnia can be dipped from the water by using
        extremely fine netting or by scooping them
        up. (Preparing a scoop is illustrated in the
        guide, p. 76)

    3. Note: Be sure not to leave great numbers of
        Daphnia closed in a tight jar or container
        for a very long time. Do not allow the con-
        tainers to sit in the direct sunlight for any
        length of time, as temperature is most critical
        to this animal! A styrofoam chest should be
        used to transport this animal any distance to
        maintain a temperature near 65°.

B. Classroom Habitats (Aquariums)

    1. Glass or plastic gallon jars, aquaria card-
        board boxes which are plastic lined, etc.
        can be used as containers.

    2. Temperature should be kept around 65° to
        80°F. (Normal room temperature of 68° to
        72°F is adequate.)

3. Don't overcrowd the containers.
    Overcrowding can be detected by death and
    observing the color of the Daphnia; that is,
    if they are dark in color, there is a lack
    of oxygen in the environment. Oxygen can be
    supplied by an aerator or by bubbling air
    through the water from a kitchen baster three
    or four times a day.

4. The aquarium should be filled with aged tap
    water, spring, well, filtered pond, or stable
    tea. (Stable tea preparation: See Section C--
    bacteria culture.)

C. Feeding and Watering

1. Daphnia feed on bacteria and algae.
    A bacteria culture can be prepared by adding
    one tablespoon of dried sheep, cow, or horse
    manure per gallon of spring, well, or fresh
    pond water and left standing for a few days.
    The yolk of an extremely hard boiled egg can
    also be used for bacteria production. Place
    only a very small amount (1 gram) of yolk in
    the container.

2. Algae such as Chlamydomonas, Euglena, and
    Chilomonas make excellent Daphnia food.
    These can be purchased from biological
    suppliers or aquarium supply stores.

3. Be sure you watch for any type of scum
    forming on the surface of the water. Remove
    this scum by pulling a paper towel across
    the surface. Note: Scum will decrease the
    oxygen supply and Daphnia will die.

D. Sexing, Culturing and Hatching

1. Most of the Daphnia population are female
    which reproduce parthenogentically. Cultures
    of Daphnia kept at room temperatures normally
    consist of only females. Females can be
    recognized by the brood pouch located above
    the intestine and to the posterior of the body.
    Males can be recognized by the near straight
    intestine.

2. Galvanized or copper vessels should not be
    used as culturing containers.

3. Place a few Daphnia from the stock culture in stable tea and maintain a temperature around 70°F or 21°C. One Daphnia will produce a brood of eggs every two or three days if they are fed properly, if the temperature is maintained at 70°F, and if overcrowding is not allowed.

4. Should the population die because of one of the above reasons, or should you want to induce the production of eggs, save the sediment as this will contain eggs called winter eggs. These can be hatched at a later time. They will need to be dried and stored in a cool place. Also, eggs can be found in the mud of streams, ponds, and lakes.

5. Winter eggs can be hatched by placing them outdoors during the season of the year when it will be thawing and freezing for several days in a two week period of time and then placing them in a container of stable tea. Also, placing the eggs in a fresh culturing medium (stable tea, etc.) should produce a quick new culture for the classroom.

Daphnia

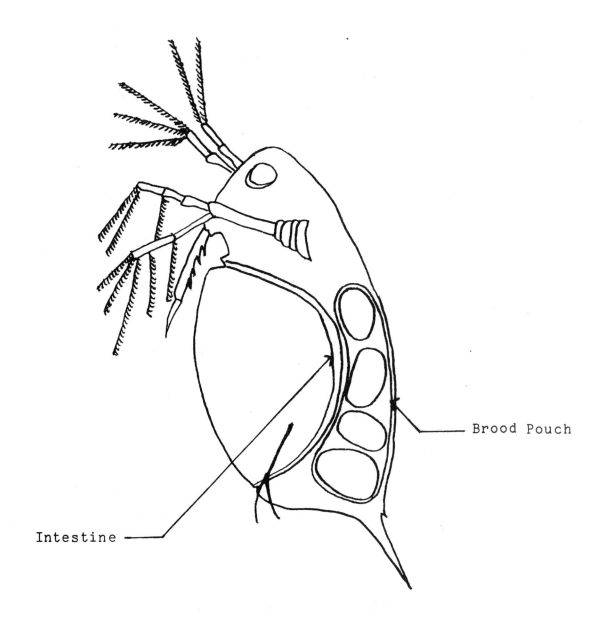

Brood Pouch

Intestine

Animals: FROGS, TOADS, AND SALAMANDERS

Phylum: Chordata (Dorsal nerve cord; gill slits tem-
          porary or permanent; never more than four legs)

Class: Amphibia (Fresh-water or terrestrial animals
          which have gills at some stage of metamorphosis.
          Some have tails and others are tailless at
          maturity.)

A. Collecting Areas and Equipment

    1. One species of frog, toad, or salamander
        can be found within the boundaries of each
        of the forty-eight states. All of the
        above animals can be found living near
        shallow water areas such as farm ponds, lakes,
        etc. After mating and egg laying these
        animals can often be found roaming through
        damp timber areas. Toads can usually be
        found around the foundation of houses, barns,
        and other buildings and in gardens. Sala-
        manders can often be found under rocks or
        other debris near a pond or swampy area.

    2. All of these animals can be caught by hand
        or with a long handled net. Place your hand
        over the top of the animal to allow you to
        grasp it firmly around the legs and body.
        Toads will usually discharge some type of
        liquid when being captured; therefore, be
        sure to wash your hands before touching any
        other part of your body or anyone else since
        it may cause irritation (not warts!).

    3. Frogs, toads, and salamanders can be trans-
        ported in plastic or glass jars, minnow
        buckets, etc. Fill the container half full
        of sphagnum moss or other small vegetation
        gathered from the pond or area where you
        have collected the amphibians. It would be
        best to take extra water for the classroom
        habitat from this area. Note: Be sure to
        keep these animals in a cool and moist
        environment while transporting them. Also,
        observe and collect some of the insects on
        which they feed from the area.

B. Classroom Habitats (Terrariums and Aquariums)

    1. Large glass aquaria suitable for fish could be used for all of these animals. Also, many other kinds of tanks can be used such as the tub part of an old washing machine, a small children's swimming pool, clear sweater boxes, etc. Don't overcrowd! Frogs will need enough water to submerge themselves at all times. Be sure to keep the water level at a constant height; that is, add water each day or so to replace that which has evaporated. Toads need a dry terrarium with a container of water so that the toad can drink or soak. Salamanders will survive best in a habitat that has the environment of a swamp or bog. A portion of the aquarium should be covered with washed sand. All of the above animals need logs and rocks which stick out of the water or lay on the sand for climbing and burrowing under. Be sure ample air is provided at all times and that the water is cleaned two or three times a week. Wash the container once a week and refill with pond, spring or well water. If none of these are available, fill with aged tap water (allowed to set 72 hours or longer). If the water should ever become cloudy, remove it immediately, wash and refill. Note: Be sure the habitat has a tight fixing cover and that it is placed in a cool area of the room. Never place toads with other animals because of the poison which some secrete.

C. Feeding and Watering

    1. Most of the animals listed above will eat insects, worms, and smaller species of their own kind. Also, many of these animals can be trained to eat other meat such as hamburger, beef and chicken liver. You may need to dangle the meat on a broom straw or something to show movement. Note: You need to have a large culture of fruit flies, mealworms, isopods, and crickets for these animals to survive for an extended time. When feeding these animals, be sure to place the insects, etc. on rocks, logs or areas where they won't get in the water and drown. Remove those that do drown immediately so that the water

doesn't become polluted. To provide a food supply, punch a hole in the lid of a fruit fly vial and lay it on the sand in the habitat. Be sure the lid is fruit fly tight but allows air into the habitat.

2. Water conditions were covered under preparing a habitat for frogs, toads, and salamanders.

D. Sexing, Breeding and Hatching

1. Sexing: Sex identification will be very difficult for those who don't know all the variations among the different species of frogs, toads, and salamanders. Therefore, it will be necessary to determine which animal and species you have of that animal class.

In frogs and toads such features may be observed as enlarged front limbs of the male, cloacal ridges of females, thumb pads (toad, during mating season only) on the first toe, discoloration of throat, male skin darker and more slimy during breeding season. Warts on females become larger and pearly white on some; and most of the male frogs and toads will make a croaking sound, mainly during the day, above or below water.

Some of the characteristics to determine the sex differences in salamanders might be that some males are smaller than the females but have a longer tail and are adorned with a temporary crest along the back of the upper surface of the tail. Most of the species of frogs, toads, and salamanders can be identified in the Golden Nature Guide--Reptiles and Amphibians where more information can be found about each species.

2. Breeding: No matter how well adapted the amphibians may be to living on land, the vast majority of them must make their way back to the water to breed. Frogs and toads return to the same pond where they were born. Salamanders go to the nearest water hole. Almost all of these animals breed in the spring and summer. Frogs and toads mount the back of the female and fertilize the

eggs as they pass from the female into the water. A male salamander will court the female for some time before depositing his spermatophore in the water so that the female can swim over it and take it into her cloaca . Also, some lay the spermotaphore on the ground, and it is picked up by the female.

3. Hatching: Frogs lay their eggs in a mass; toads lay theirs in continuous string; and the salamanders lay eggs one at a time. Also, some female species will continue to carry the young internally or in pouches for different lengths of time. Hatching into the tadpole stage will take from several days to several weeks in different species. If you collect eggs or order eggs to hatch in the classroom, you should keep them in a habitat of natural pond water or 10% Holfreters solution. Each dish should have only five to ten eggs per dish. As the tadpoles hatch you should place some elodea or filamentous algae (this can be collected from ponds) in each container for food and oxygen. Also, you might feed them a small amount of lettuce or boiled cabbage twice a week. The cooler you keep the embryos the slower the development; therefore, by keeping them cool the children will get a chance to see more stages of development. Note: Should the water become cloudy or foul smelling at anytime, remove the good eggs to another container. Also, be sure to replenish the water of these habitats with the same type of water. Never allow their container to be placed in direct sunlight for any length of time.

Stages of Development of the Frog

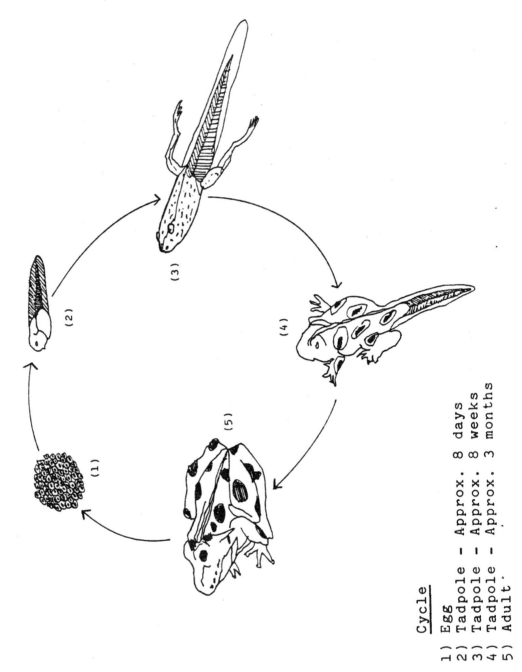

Cycle

1) Egg
2) Tadpole – Approx. 8 days
3) Tadpole – Approx. 8 weeks
4) Tadpole – Approx. 3 months
5) Adult

Animal: FRUIT FLY

Phylum: Anthropoda (Terrestrial aerial and aquatic forms;
          segmented bodies and chitenous exoskeletons)

Class: Insecta (Head, thorax, and abdomen; six legs;
          one pair of antennae)

A. Collecting Areas and Equipment

    1. Fruit flies are widely scattered throughout
        the world. At least 2,000 species have been
        found half of which live in Hawaii. They are
        often found in breweries, pickling plants,
        in bars and restaurants, stores that sell
        fruit, and in many homes. Other fruit flies
        feed on fungi or decaying plants. They are
        most abundant during the summer and autumn.
        Fruit flies can be cheaply purchased from
        biological suppliers.

    2. Fruit flies can easily be collected in a
        bottle that has a piece of well-ripened
        banana sprinkled with a little dry yeast with
        a funnel made of paper taped to the mouth of
        the bottle. Also, be sure your trap is well
        lighted from the bottom as fruit flies are
        attracted to light. Note: <u>The funnel should
        have only about 1/8 of an inch opening.</u>

B. Classroom Habitats

    1. Any type of clear glass or plastic container
        could be used to house the fruit fly. Be sure
        the lid fits tightly and that the air opening
        is escape proof. Pill vials and olive jars make
        excellent containers for students. A hole can
        be punched through the plastic top on pill
        vials and a guaze strip taped to the opening
        for air. Cotton and other type substances can
        be used as stoppers for other jars.

    2. Be sure to place inside the jar something like
        a piece of paper towel on which larvae can climb.

3. Fruit flies need an optimum temperature of 70° to 75°F. Note: <u>Be sure to keep them out of direct sunlight or extreme heat.</u>

C. Feeding and Watering

1. A prepared medium purchased from a biological supplier is the best food for classroom use. However, canned pumpkin, banana or banana mixed with agar, and fruit pulps which are fermenting can be used. Yeast can be sprinkled on the fruit to speed up fermentation.

2. Note: <u>Be sure the medium is kept moist but not wet.</u>

D. Sexing, Breeding, and Hatching

1. The male fruit flies will have a comb-like structure on each of the four front legs that might be seen with the naked eye, but surely could be seen with a magnifier or microscope.

2. Mating will occur only if the female is mature and the male is of the same species. Before mating, a male fruit fly courts the female by running around the female vibrating one or both wings, licks her, and, if he is of the right species, they mate. Twelve hours after the adult fruit flies mate, the female begins to lay batches of 15 to 20 white eggs each day, continuing until she has laid 400-900.

3. Fruit flies go through the complete metamorphosis--egg, larva, pupa, and adult stages. The fruit fly egg will hatch about 24 hours after it is laid. The next stages, larva and pupa, will take about 10 to 14 days.

Stages of Development of a Fruit Fly

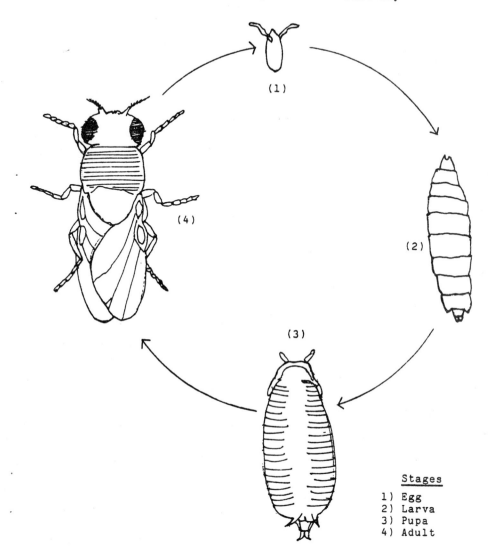

Stages
1) Egg
2) Larva
3) Pupa
4) Adult

Animal: GUPPIES

Phylum: Chordata (Animals which possess a notochord, usually temporary, and a dorsal nerve cord)

Class: Pisces (True fish--fresh water and marine forms; lay numerous eggs and give live birth)

A. Collecting Area and Equipment

    1. Guppies are present in large numbers in fresh-water areas of the Central American Caribbean Islands, Barbados, and Trinidad. Therefore, most of us will need to purchase ours at pet shops, from friends, and biology supply houses. It is best to purchase them as near home as possible.

B. Classroom Habitat

    1. Large pickle jars, glass aquaria (size is important) and plastic lined cardboard boxes (see illustration, p. 81) can be used for containers. Approximately one gallon of water per fish is a good rule of thumb. Temperature of the water should be kept about normal room temperature (approximately 70° to 74°F). If you have large numbers of fish, a mechanical aerator should be installed. However, if you have just a few and a large surface area of water, no aerator is needed. (Note: Small opening fish bowls which allow for very little water surface should not be used, because they cut down on the amount of oxygen that can be dissolved. Also, increased temperature of the water will decrease the amount of dissolved oxygen.) Don't place the habitat in direct sunlight or near heat registers. You can use a kitchen baster to pump air through the water a few times each morning and night to increase dissolved oxygen. Growing plants add color to aquariums and assist in replenishing the oxygen supply. Also, some plants serve as a food supply.

C. Feeding and Watering

1. Most tropicals need to be fed only a very small
    pinch of food once a day. Avoid overfeeding
    and polluting the water with excess food mater-
    ials. A variety of foods, dry and alive, are
    good for any population. Daphnia or Brine shrimp
    make excellent live food. Water level should
    be kept the same by adding distilled, spring,
    well, or aged tap water for that lost due to
    evaporating. Note: <u>Always be sure the water is</u>
    <u>the same temperature as that in the tank or</u>
    <u>aquarium before filling</u>!

D. Sexing, Breeding and Hatching

1. Male guppies will be smaller than female in
    length and over all size. Also, the male will
    be multi-color and the female will be largely a
    whitish color. The anal fin, called gonopodium,
    is modified for transferring sperm to the female.
    The female will show black spots near her anal
    fin when she is expecting a new brood.

2. Guppies will start breeding when they reach
    about one inch in length and the male shows
    the development of a gonodopodium. Courtship
    can be observed when male and female guppy are
    placed in an aquarium about one day apart.
    Place the male in first. You should be able to
    observe courtship start in a very short time
    after adding the female. After mating, the
    female may continue to give birth to several
    broods without further mating.

3. The eggs will hatch within the mother and
    young will be born alive. It takes between
    23 to 28 days or longer for the female to
    give birth. One indication that she is about
    to give birth is the swollen abdomen and dark
    patches near the anal fin. Note: <u>Great amounts</u>
    <u>of plant material in the aquarium during birth</u>
    <u>may deter the female from eating the newly born</u>.
    Also, reduce crowding and a maternity cage may
    assist in obtaining live births.

Animal: HERMIT CRAB

Phylum: Arthropoda (Terrestrial, aerial and aquatic
          forms; segmented bodies and chitenous shells)

Class: Crustacea (Exoskeleton is hardened)

A.   Collecting Areas and Equipment

    1.   Hermit crabs are semi-terrestrial and found
         along the tropical coasts. Bermuda and Florida
         coasts would be two areas for collecting.
         Several species of this crab can be found
         climbing on or living near plants. The Hermit
         Crab can be handled by hand but one must be
         careful to place the fingers so that the crab
         can't pinch them. Also be careful not to
         drop the crab and break its shell. You might
         prefer to use kitchen tongs to pick them up.

B.   Classroom Habitat

    1.   Any type of glass aquarium or clear plastic
         container would make an excellent habitat for
         the hermit crab. The bottom should be covered
         with soil, sand, and rocks. Provide a container
         of water such as a plastic butter container.
         Some sticks and plants for the crabs to crawl
         on might be interesting and beneficial. Note:
         Be sure to cover with a lid that will allow
         air in the terrarium and be escape proof.

C.   Feeding and Watering

    1.   Hermit crabs are mainly omnivorous scavengers
         which feed on small animals and plants. They
         are not heavy eaters; therefore don't place
         too much food in their habitats at one time.
         Small pieces of fruits, garden vegetables, and
         maybe an occasional mealworm would be enough.
         Be sure they have a clean container of water
         at all times.

D. Sexing, Breeding, and Hatching

1. The sexes differ externally only in the form
    of the swimmerets which have differing functions.
    The male will have only two pairs of swimmerets
    which are used for transferring the sperm. Fe-
    males will have four pairs of swimmerets that
    are well supplied with setae to which the eggs
    are attached after they have been laid and
    fertilized. Also, some sources indicate that
    you can determine the male by looking at the
    apron under the cephalothorax. If it is very
    narrow and pointed, it is a male.

2. Most crabs breed throughout the year. At this
    time sperm is transferred to the female by the
    modified swimmerets mentioned in paragraph one
    of this part. This is thought to be much like
    crayfish fertilization, where the male spreads
    a sticky seminal fluid over the swimmeret region
    of the female.

3. Crabs which have thousands of eggs attached
    to the swimmerets, in berry as they are called,
    can be seen partially out of their shells
    fanning their swimmerets over the eggs to
    aerate them. As the larvae hatch, moulting
    at the same time to become zoea larvae, the
    mother will sit partly out of her shell to
    wipe the swimmerets of the larvae with the
    bristles on her small fourth pair of legs.
    After moulting four times, the young hermit
    crab will seek a snail shell for the first
    home. The above growth stages take four to
    five days to complete and an additional year
    or more for sexual maturity to be reached.

Animal: ISOPODS (SOWBUGS: PILLBUGS)

Phylum: Arthropoda (Terrestrial, aerial and aquatic
         forms; segmented bodies and chitenous exoskeletons)

Class: Crustacea (Crust-like shell formed by hardened
         calcareous deposits)

A. Collecting Area and Equipment

   1. Isopods can be collected in dark, damp areas
       which are near decaying vegetation, rotten
       fruits, rotten wood, etc. Such places might
       be under rocks, logs, piles of grass clippings,
       compost piles, etc.

   2. Any type of container which has a tight lid
       in which small holes can be punched can be used
       to collect and transport isopods. Coffee cans
       and plastic butter trays would be excellent.
       Holes in the lid need to be small so that the
       animals won't crawl out. These holes can
       handily be made by heating a paper clip point
       over a candle and punching it through the
       plastic.

   3. Collecting can be by hand, scoop or by brush-
       ing. Isopods are so slow moving that you can
       easily pick them up by hand. A plastic scoop
       can be used to scoop a thin layer of dirt
       under rocks which may have large number isopods.
       Also, your plastic container can be held under
       the edge of a rock and isopods brushed into the
       container.

B. Classroom Habitat (Terrarium)

   1. Aquariums, fish bowls, plastic lined cardboard
       boxes, etc. can be used to house these animals
       in the classroom.

   2. Place several inches of rich humus soil mixed
       with gravel on the bottom of the container with
       a few flat rocks spread over the area; several
       pieces of wood, or crumpled cardboard, should
       be spread throughout the soil.

3. Some type of screening and lid must be provided to make it escape proof and to prevent the evaporation of too much moisture. Moisture is most critical for breathing.

4. Temperature should be 65 to 75°F. Normal room temperature is adequate.

5. A hiding place is necessary for protection from enemies and members of its own kind during the period that isopods molt.

C. Feeding and Watering

1. Isopods should be fed about once every two months. Note: <u>Don't overfeed</u>.

2. Decaying vegetation, half a potato or apple, and oatmeal make excellent foods. Place foods other than decaying vegetation in a low plastic tray. Note: <u>Be sure not to leave moldy feed in the container</u>.

3. Be sure the soil is kept moist at all times.

D. Sexing, Breeding and Hatching

1. The sexes are usually distinguished by secondary characteristics associated with the transfer of sperm and the protection of eggs and young. You can easily spot a female by the brood pouch which appears as a white triangular patch between the female's forelegs. About 20 or more eggs are laid in the pouch, which becomes slightly distended. The pouch is transparent, so the eggs can be easily seen with a hand lens.

2. Isopods collected in early fall should mate and produce eggs by midwinter (around February).

3. Hatching will occur about 3 weeks after the eggs are laid if the temperature is kept around 72°F; the brood pouch will slit to allow the young to escape.

4. The newly born young will shed their skins immediately after birth and proceed to eat the skins for their first meal.

Animal: MEALWORM

Phylum: Arthropoda (Terrestrial, aerial and aquatic forms; segmented bodies and chitenous exoskeletons)

Class: Insecta (Head, thorax, and abdomen; six legs; one pair of antennae)

A. Collecting Area and Equipment

 1. Mealworms can easily be found in grain elevators, warehouses, etc., where grain and meal products are stored or are being processed. However, for school purposes it would probably be easier to purchase your mealworms from a biological supplier and start your own culture. The mealworm beetle, larva, and pupa, can easily be caught by hand in an area where they feed. Also, laying two sheets of paper together with feed, such as oatmeal, bran, etc. will draw the animals between papers and you can shake off the oatmeal and pick off or brush the larva into a container. Plastic containers, ice cream containers, and butter trays filled half full of oatmeal can be used for collecting and transporting these animals.

B. Classroom Habitats

 1. Habitats for the classroom or for culturing these animals can be metal or plastic flower boxes, five gallon buckets, enamel pans, crockery jars, gallon jars (either plastic or glass), etc. A medium of shredded paper and bran or oatmeal should be placed two or three inches deep in the habitat. Also, pieces of burlap to cover will help retain moisture in the medium.

 2. Be sure the habitat is located in the room where it will have a temperature of about 75° to 80°F.

C. Feeding and Watering

 1. Bran used for livestock, oatmeal, cream of wheat and other types of meal can be used as food. Half of a potato placed on top of the meal adds some variety and moisture for the mealworm.

2. No water needs to be supplied for these animals as they have a physiological process for making water from carbohydrate foods; the potato will supplement their needs. Be sure not to allow the dry food to mold. Should the food mold transfer the larvae, pupae, and adults to a new medium and container.

3. Place new meal in the habitat two or three times a year and a new potato as often as the other appears to be dried out or mostly consumed.

D. Sexing, Breeding, and Hatching

1. The male beetle can be recognized in some species by the slightly longer antennae. However, most species have no external characteristics which are obvious to distinguish the male from the female.

2. The mature beetles will mate, and the female will lay eggs if the habitat has a good supply of moisture. When you see several adults moving about the habitat be sure to add several pieces of apple or potato to increase the moisture available for laying. The female will normally lay 500 to 600 eggs if conditions are right.

3. Mealworm larvae hatch from tiny oval shaped white eggs that are usually covered with food particles and debris. The hatching time is approximately one week after the eggs are laid. Mealworms will shed or molt their skin several times during the next three months or so. The life cycle time will depend largely on the environmental conditions of food, temperature, and moisture. However, the larva stage will last about two to four months, the pupal stage will be from one to three weeks, and the adults may live two months or so.

Stages of Development of a Mealworm

(2)

(1)

(3)

(4)

Stages

1) Egg
2) Larva
3) Pupa
4) Adult

Animal: PRAYING MANTISES

Phylum: Arthropoda (Terrestrial, aerial, and aquatic
          forms; segmented bodies and chitenous exoskeletons)

Class: Insecta (Head, thorax, and abdomen; six legs; one
          pair of antennae)

A. Collecting Areas and Equipment

    1. The praying mantis is considered a cosmopolitan
        insect found around the world except for some
        of the frigid areas. The egg cases will be found
        attached securely around the twigs or stems of
        plants that can withstand the extreme wind, hail,
        and other environmental conditions of the area.
        These egg cases will have a frothy looking texture
        and globular or elongated shape. Their size could
        be from the size of a pencil eraser to a walnut or
        larger. In the fall of the year you can find the
        adult clinging to window screens, porch railings,
        street signs, and in areas where there is a good
        food supply. Also, the adult might be found
        hunting near lighted porches or street lamps.

    2. Any type container that is large enough to hold
        the animal for a few hours can be used for trans-
        porting. Plastic gallon pickle jars, etc., would
        make excellent collecting containers. The animal
        is harmless to handle; therefore one can pick them
        up and place them in a container. Also, one could
        use tongs to grasp them back of the strong front
        legs.

B. Classroom Habitats

    1. Since the insect is so large, the cage must be
        large enough to allow the animal comfortable
        space in which to move about so that it doesn't
        injure its wings. Fish aquaria, terraria, boxes
        with sides cut and lined with nylon netting, etc.
        are excellent cages. These cages should be
        covered with a netting or wire mesh top. The cages
        should not have any materials on the bottom, such
        as soil, sand, etc., that would afford their
        prey hiding places. Twigs or branches should be

placed in the cage for climbing and resting areas. Note: <u>Be sure these twigs and branches allow free movement without injury to the mantis wings</u>.

C. Feeding and Watering

1. The praying mantis will eat almost any type of insect, including its own kind. Grasshoppers, flies, and crickets would be some of the best and easier found insects for food. Fruit flies would be, by far, the easiest to culture for food; however it would take several hundred a day to feed the mantis. Mantis don't prefer mealworms but will eat them so one could feed them a combination of mealworms and fruit flies. (The guide explains how to culture both.)

2. Mantis drink a lot of water, so pet insects or insects brought indoors more often die of dehydration than from lack of food. Water should be sprayed or sprinkled on the sides of the cage or on twigs and foliage that has been placed in the cage. Note: <u>A mantis could, but may not, learn to drink out of a dish of water placed in the cage</u>.

D. Sexing, Breeding and Hatching

1. In the fall might be the only time that one can easily distinguish the sexes. The female's abdomen becomes extremely distended with eggs. The male remains very slim. During the mating process the male has to be very careful to approach the female unobserved from the rear and cautiously leave in a like manner, or the female may grab and eat him. Sometimes the male is killed and consumed during the mating act. The male and female usually cling together for several hours, during which a capsule that contains spermatozoa which later will fertilize her eggs is transferred to the female. The eggs are then laid several days later, and the female has nothing more to do with the offspring. The eggs will hatch into nymphs about four or five weeks after the eggs have been brought indoors or the temperature outside has warmed. The eggs can be kept in a refrigerator until the time you want to hatch them. Note: <u>The nymphs need immediate food when they hatch and the humidity must be kept high by watering the plant(s) and sides of the cage</u>.

Animal: SNAILS (POND AND LAND)

Phylum: Mollusca (Terrestrial, fresh water, and marine
          forms; usually have a calcareous shell covering
          the soft body)

Class: Gastropoda (Flat-footed, with or without coiled
          shells)

A. Collecting Areas and Equipment

　　1. Pond snails can be collected in some parts of
        any fresh-water areas. One can find them on the
        moss in shallow water areas, on sticks, leaves,
        etc. They can be picked up by hand or collected
        by net, strainers, or scoops. Any type of plastic
        jug would make an excellent transporting container.
        Also, heavy plastic bags would work for transport-
        ing. Be sure to take along extra water and some
        of the small plant life of the area.

　　2. Land snails can best be found in a garden or
        damp area which is heavily covered with decaying
        wood, leaves, etc.

　　3. Snails can also be purchased from biological
        supply houses listed in the guide, p.89.

B. Classroom Habitat

　　1. Pond snails can be housed in any type of glass
        aquarium, fish bowl, or plastic containers such
        as shoe boxes, sweater boxes, etc. Don't use
        metal containers for permanent housing. Any of
        the containers should have the bottom covered with
        an inch or so of washed sand and some water plants.
        The water should be pond, spring, or well water
        and about one-third of the water should be changed
        every two weeks or so. Note: Be sure the water
        temperature is the same when refilling the con-
        tainer.

　　2. Land snails can use any of the above containers
        as a terrarium. Be sure to collect some rocks,
        sticks, logs, leaves, soil, and some small plants
        from the area where you find the snail. Be sure
        to keep the soil moist but not soaking wet at
        all times. Place a container of water somewhere

in the terrarium to keep the humidity high, and
provided a rather tight lid to keep in moisture
and snails. Should mold start to form, allow
more air to enter the container.

C. Feeding and Watering

1. Pond snails will eat algae, water plants, dry
    fish food, and lettuce or cabbage pieces. Be
    sure to maintain a constant water level by adding
    pond, spring, well water, or aged tap water that
    is the same temperature.

2. Land snails will feed on leaves from trees and
    on most garden plants such as lettuce and cabbage.
    Limestone rock placed in the terrarium will also
    serve as calcium for shell growth. In order for
    these snails to stay active, they must be kept in
    a high humidity. Don't overwater the container.

D. Sexing, Breeding and Hatching

1. Both pond and land snails are hermaphroditic
    (i.e., each individual snail has both male and
    female organs opening to the exterior).

2. The mating season of pond and land snails starts
    in early spring. Two snails will come along
    side each other and pass sperm from one individual
    to the other individual. However, some snails do
    have the capability of fertilizing themselves.
    Some are ready for breeding again after three to
    ten weeks, and others take several months.

3. Eggs will be laid in gelatinous masses which are
    attached to leaves, stems, and other objects until
    hatching in one to three weeks. Always be sure
    that these eggs are kept in water of the same
    temperature! Snail eggs are excellent to observe
    in terms of development, because the egg membrane
    is transparent so the student can see inside with
    a hand lens or microscope. Newborn snails can be
    fed the same as adults.

PLANTS

The plants listed and described in this section will be used mainly in aquaria or terraria as food, oxygen generators, users of waste, protection of the young, egg-laying areas, and decoration. Also, some can be used for population experiments.

Plant: ALGAE

Phylum: Thallophytes (Simple plants that are without
          stems, roots, or leaves and may be one or
          multi-celled in form)

Class: (Many classes could be listed here as to color
          and non-color)

A. Collecting Areas and Equipment

    1. Algae can be found in both fresh water and
        marine type environments. Also, it is
        possible to find some types of algae growing
        on moist walls in cities, or on patches of
        bare soil after a rain. Marine forms of
        algae are more common, more attractive, and
        the largest in size and number.

        Any shore line will provide some form of algae
        which can be collected by hand, nets, scoops,
        large mouth plastic jars, etc. However, it
        is best to wade out and get some forms before
        they are damaged by the tide action. The
        fresh water algae can be collected by using
        small vials (all the collecting equipment one
        really needs); scraping the greenish fuzz or
        stain from wood, rocks, soil, or bark; using
        nets, depth controlled sampling jars, etc.
        Note: <u>Be sure all water species are placed
        in water immediately, preferably that from
        which they were taken. Be sure all other
        forms are kept damp and not in direct sunlight
        or near intense heat.</u>

    2. All forms of these can be purchased from the
        biological suppliers listed in Appendix B.

    3. If collecting is done during temperatures
        above 75°F, be sure to transport materials
        in insulated containers such as inexpensive
        styrofoam picnic chests, and keep out of
        direct sunlight.

B.   Classroom Habitats

    1.   Keeping a supply of algae on hand for study
        is not a difficult matter. If collecting
        vials are opened, specimens can be kept
        alive for several days. If keeping them for
        a longer time is desired, then one should
        place the specimens in a larger container
        such as aquaria, gallon jars, etc. Place in
        area of moderate light and cover loosely.
        Temperatures between 40°F and 70°F are ideal,
        but at no time should the temperature go
        above 75°F.

C.   Watering and Feeding

    1.   Water Forms: The container should contain
        at least twice as much space for water as
        plant materials--preferably much more water
        space. Some extra water from the collecting
        area should be gathered at the time of
        collecting. This original water--spring,
        well, pond, distilled, aged water (if one
        must use it) or salt water--should be used
        to keep the container water at the same level
        at all times. Preparations are available
        from pet stores and biological supply houses
        to make the salt water solution.

    2.   Land Forms: Different types of mediums can
        be purchased to use in culturing simple
        algaes. A good garden soil type medium can
        be used in growing algae. Note: <u>Just be</u>
        <u>sure it hasn't been recently fertilized.</u>

D.   Reproduction

    1.   Blue-green marine algae reproduce by simple
        cell division. The Brown algae may reproduce
        by spores or by vegetative propagation in
        which fragments of the plants are broken off
        by water action, etc. Also, some reproduce by
        sperm and egg cells being produced in small
        cavities on the parent plant and released to
        fuse and form new plants.

    2.   Fresh water algae most often reproduces by
        an asexual form called fission, i.e.
        dividing of a cell.

Plant: ANACHARIS (ELODEA)

Phylum: Spermatophyta (A plant that produces seeds)

Class: Monocotyledon (Embryo with one cotyledon)

A. Collecting Areas and Equipment

1. Species of this plant can be found in the
    Great Plains, the Rocky Mountains, and the
    Pacific States, etc. Anacharis occurs in
    abundance in lakes, ponds, canals, and the
    slow moving water of streams and rivers.
    It can be found in submerged soil at all
    water depths up to about ten to eleven
    meters.

2. These plants can be collected by pulling
    them from the mud or breaking off pieces.
    Note: Be sure the plants are kept in water
    at all times.

B. Classroom Habitat

1. Any type of plastic or glass aquarium can
    be used to grow anacharis. You will find
    that this plant grows much too fast when
    rooted in a small aquarium. Therefore let
    it float loosely on the surface of the water.
    Fresh spring or well water would be prefer-
    able for this type of aquarium. However,
    aged tap water and filtered pond water can
    be used. One could have some problems with
    chemicals in tap water and with animals that
    feed on plants in pond water. Note: Be
    sure all plants are washed thoroughly with
    cold water before being placed in the
    aquarium.

C. Feeding and Watering

1. Commercial food for plants can be purchased
    from biological suppliers. Mag Amp is one
    such food for Anacharis (Elodea). See
    Appendix B.

2. Be sure to keep an adequate water level for plants replacing the evaporated water with spring, well, pond, or aged tap water.

D. Reproduction

1. Vegetative propagation, i.e. by broken off shoots, is one way that anacharis (elodea) grows. Also, there are male and female flowers; the male plant produces micro-spores which float to the female flower on the surface of the water.

Plant: FERN (Mostly terrestrial plants with true roots, stems, and leaves with vascular systems; reproduce by spores and alternate generations)

Phylum: Pteriodophyta (Nonflowering plants having creeping or erect rhizomes or an erect aerial stem and large conspicuous leaves)

A. Collecting Areas and Equipment

1. Ferns are widely distributed throughout the world, but the majority grow in the tropics.

2. A sharp spade and some type of bucket or container to transport them in is all the equipment needed for collection. Be sure to get a piece of the underground stem.

3. Be sure to collect some of the soil and to record the habitat conditions of the area.

B. Classroom Habitats (Terraria)

1. Any watertight container with transparent sides that is large enough to allow for the accommodation of the plants selected can be used. When indoors, fern plants require a reasonably bright location, but do avoid direct sunlight; they flourish under fluorescent lighting. They grow best at temperatures between 60°F to 70°F and will endure temperatures as high as 75°F if the air is moving and humid. In the back of this guide is a drawing of an inexpensive table that can be used to hang a fluorescent light and allow for rolling the terrarium to warmer or cooler areas of the room or building during the day or weekends.

2. The bottom of the container (habitat) should be covered with a layer of loose rocks or gravel to provide root drainage and aeration. Since most plants in this type terrarium require an acidic growing medium, the top soil should be prepared by placing a layer of peat moss over the rocks and then covering the peat moss with a mixture of one part garden loam, one part sand, and one part peat moss.

C. Feeding and Watering

   1. Biological suppliers have prepared plant food
       such as Nasco's Mag Amp fertilizer. Local pet
       stores might have some plant food for terraria.

   2. Ferns should be watered often enough to keep
       the soil evenly moist and the vegetation should
       be sprayed with a fine mist each day. Note:
       A clean pump spray window cleaner bottle would
       make an excellent sprayer.

D. Reproduction

   1. To grow ferns from spores, fill a small, clean
       flowerpot or container (with hole in bottom)
       with a mixture of prepared medium or see
       Section B-2. Place the pot on a tray or
       saucer of water and let stand until the
       medium has become thoroughly moistened. Get
       some sori from the bottom of fern leaves and
       release the spores by tearing the sori apart
       with needles. Dust the spores over the top
       of the moistened dirt and cover with a sheet
       of glass or plastic. Note: Be sure the tray
       or saucer is filled with water at all times.
       In a warm, moderately lighted place (not
       intense sunlight) the spores should begin to
       grow in a few weeks. After the ferns have
       made a good start they can be transplanted in
       the terrarium.

   2. Vegetative propagation is another way of
       starting your plants. Simply dig up a plant
       with part of the rhizome and rhizoids
       attached and transplant in prepared medium
       or the medium suggested in part B of this
       section.

Plant: MOSS

Phylum: Bryophyta (Multicellular green plants; alter-
          nate generations without vascular system;
          reproduce by spores)

Class: Musci (Either creeping or erect plants with
          leafy stem)

A. Collecting Areas and Equipment

   1. Mosses are quite cosmopolitan in distribution;
       they can be found in every state in the United
       States and Canada. The largest mosses in the
       United States can be found in the evergreen
       forests of the west coast. Several species
       of moss can be found in timber and forest
       habitats. However, some moss species prefer
       full sunshine, some high altitudes, some
       seashores, and for some, one must wade waist-
       deep in ponds, or reach out of boats to
       collect.

   2. A knife and some type of carrying container
       will be adequate equipment for collecting.
       Note: Be sure to bring along an adequate
       amount of soil or whatever medium it is
       growing on or in at the time; try to keep
       the conditions about the same in your habitat
       as that of the area from which it was collected.

B. Classroom Habitat (Terrarium)

   1. Any watertight container with transparent
       sides that is large enough to accommodate
       the selected materials can be used for a
       terrarium. The terrarium will need to have
       the bottom surface covered with a course
       material, such as gravel, to provide drainage
       and root aeration. The bottom course of
       materials should be covered with three parts
       soil (humus) and one part sand.

   2. Mosses, ferns, liverworts, and lichens can
       be planted. Note: Be sure not to overcrowd

the plants; wet the roots before planting. After planting the materials be sure to spray the entire area with water and cover with plastic or glass.

3.   The terrarium should be placed in an area which is well lighted and cool (68 F). Note: Direct sunlight or excessive heat could be very harmful.

C. Feeding and Watering

1.   Certain species of mosses will need added nutrients in a closed environment of this nature; therefore, one can buy from biological suppliers such nutrients as Mag Amp or other mediums. (See Appendix)

2.   Maintain a water level as high as the gravel under the soil. Stop watering and remove the cover for awhile if moisture covers the sides so that you cannot see in, or if the water runs down the container's sides continuously.

D. Reproduction

1.   The green moss plant reproduces sexually by producing eggs and sperm in special organs found at the tip of the plant. During sexual reproduction, the sperm must swim to the egg; this explains the need for a moist environment for this plant. The fertilized egg grows into a mature plant which develops a tip that produces spores. These spores are then released and scattered by the wind. When favorable conditions are reached by the spores they grow into new green moss plants which reproduce sexually.

Plant: SAGITTARIA (ARROWHEAD)

Phylum: Spermatophyta (A plant that produces seed)

Class: Monocotydelon (Embryo with one cotyledon)

A. Collecting Areas and Equipment

1. Common habitat areas for Sagittaria are fresh water marshes, pond margins, lake shorelines, and shallow water areas from Ohio to South Dakota, south to New Mexico, Louisiana, and Tennessee. Plants are found widely spread in Kansas and make an excellent aquarium plant.

2. Since Sagittaria is a rooted plant, some type of spade should be used to dig up the roots. Note: Be sure to keep the plants wrapped in wet newspaper, etc., while transporting them.

3. These plants can be purchased from most biological suppliers on the list in this guide. (See Appendix)

B. Classroom Habitats

1. Any type of plastic or glass aquaria which will allow adequate light to enter and hold water could be used. Also, a plastic swimming pool set-up like the one illustrated in the equipment section of this guide could be used. (See Appendix)

2. Two to three inches of mud from the area where the plants were collected or sand can be used to plant Sagittaria. Note: Be sure the mud or sand is not heaped higher than the crown. The crown is the place where the leaves start to branch.

3. Be sure to keep the moisture conditions like that of a swamp. Place the aquarium in a well lighted area but not in direct sunlight.

The temperature should be kept around normal
room temperature--68° to 72°F. If the room
is to be colder than this over a week-end,
one might place a light bulb over the
aquarium for that time period and cover the
aquarium with a thin plastic sheet. (See
Appendix)

C. Feeding and Watering

    1. Nutrients can be purchased from biological
       suppliers or pet stores that will enhance the
       growth and plant population.

    2. Water is the most important environmental factor in
       plant growth, so be sure to cover the plant
       container with plastic or glass over extended
       time periods so that evaporation will be
       decreased.

D. Reproduction

    1. During the normal growing season most species
       of Sagittaria reproduce freely by means of long
       stolons (horizontal branches or runners) which
       root and develop a new plant at each node.

Plant: VALLISNERIA (EELGRASS OR WATER CELERY)

Phylum: Spermatophyta (A plant that produces seed)

Class: Monocotyledon (Embryo with one cotyledon)

A. Collecting Areas and Equipment

1. Eelgrass is considered to be quite cosmopolitan as to growing areas. However, eelgrass is mainly abundant in the warmer regions of the world. Quiet water areas of ponds or lakes which are about one meter deep will usually have a heavy underwater growth of eelgrass.

2. Eelgrass will be rooted in the muddy bottom of ponds, etc; therefore you may need a sharp spade to cut the plant loose from the bottom and retain some of the roots. One can possibly pull some of the younger, less mature plants by hand. Note: <u>Be sure they are kept damp at all times, either in a container of water or wrapped in a wet towel, etc.</u>

B. Classroom Habitat

1. Any type of large aquarium or other container which will allow the total plant to be submerged in water and the roots buried in soil can be used for the habitat. The best water for the habitat would be well, spring, filtered pond or aged tap water.

2. Place the habitat in good light but not direct sunlight or excessive heat. Normal room temperature should be maintained. You may want to use a grow-lite to maintain this temperature.

3. Note: Do not heap the sand or soil around the plants higher than the crown. The crown is the place where the leaves start to branch out.

C. Feeding and Watering

    1. Plant nutrients can be purchased from biological
suppliers that will enhance the health of the
plants and help in providing more feed for some
of the animals.

    2. Water level should be kept reasonably constant
at all times, i.e., the evaporated water should
be replaced with spring, well, filtered pond, or
aged tap water.

D. Reproduction

    1. Eelgrass reproduces asexually and sexually.
Asexually, eelgrass is spread vegetatively by
stolons to increase the population of plants.
Sexually, the eelgrass produces two flowers--
the male flower which produces pollen and the
female flower which grows seeds. If the seeds
are to grow, a pollen grain must enter the
female flower. Since the male and female plants
are totally submerged in water, it is necessary
for the female flower to surface for pollination
and for the male to break off and surface to
release the pollen for pollination. Pollen is
transferred to the female plant on the water
surface by wind and insects. When enough
pollen grains have been carried to the female
flower, the coil spring stalk pulls the female
flower under the water where the seeds will
develop.

Plant: WOLFFIA (DUCKWEED)

Phylum: Spermatophyta (A plant that produces seed)

Class: Monocotyledon (Embryo with one cotyledon)

A. Collecting Areas and Equipment

    1. Different species can be found in the slow
        moving water of streams, ponds, stagnant water
        holes, or pools. Duckweed is a very small
        floating perennial consisting of a thallus-like
        stem without leaves and with or without roots.
        Flowers are very small and are seldom found.
        Duckweed is often found covering the tops of
        aquariums in pet supply stores or fish ponds.

    2. It can be collected in vials, bottles or
        plastic bags by simply holding the container
        under water and letting the Duckweed flow into
        the container.

B. Classroom Habitat

    1. Any of the following containers could be used
        to house duckweed--plastic butter dishes, plastic
        shoe boxes, sweater boxes, baby food jars,
        regular fish bowls or aquaria, etc.

C. Feeding and Watering

    1. Plant nutrients can be purchased from biological
        suppliers which will enhance the growth and
        health of your plants.

    2. The water level of the container should be kept
        adequately high at all times. Well or spring
        water would be the best to add back for evaporated
        water; however you can use aged tap water of
        filtered pond water.

D. Reproduction

    1. Propagation is generally by lateral 'shoots'
        which readily break free from the parent plant.
        Duckweed does flower, extremely inconspicuously,
        and produce a globular looking seed that is
        slightly compressed, smooth, with a spongy outer
        layer.

EQUIPMENT IDEAS

Fruit Fly Transfer Chamber

To transfer fruit flies from the purchased culture vial: Make holes
in the sides of the chamber for vials. Cover the chamber with clear
plastic wrap. Insert one or more vials containing medium (See p. 39)
to receive fruit flies for individual student use. Insert culture
vial in remaining hole. Allow fruit flies to enter the plastic
covered chamber. To cause fruit flies to enter students' vials,
cover the chamber with an opaque substance. Remove vials with
fruit flies. Plug vials and holes with cotton or gauze.

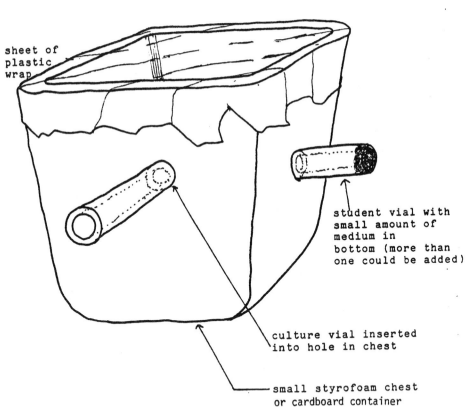

sheet of opaque
material (e.g. book
or black paper)

sheet of
plastic
wrap

student vial with
small amount of
medium in
bottom (more than
one could be added)

culture vial inserted
into hole in chest

small styrofoam chest
or cardboard container

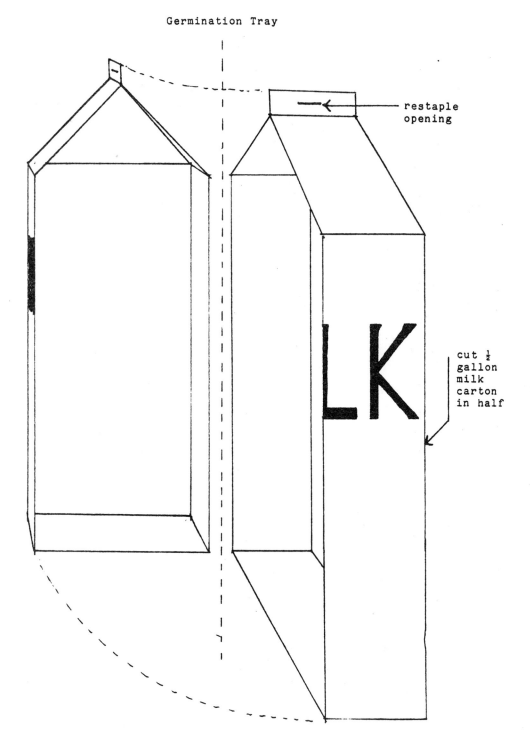

Germination Tray

restaple opening

cut ½ gallon milk carton in half

LK

72

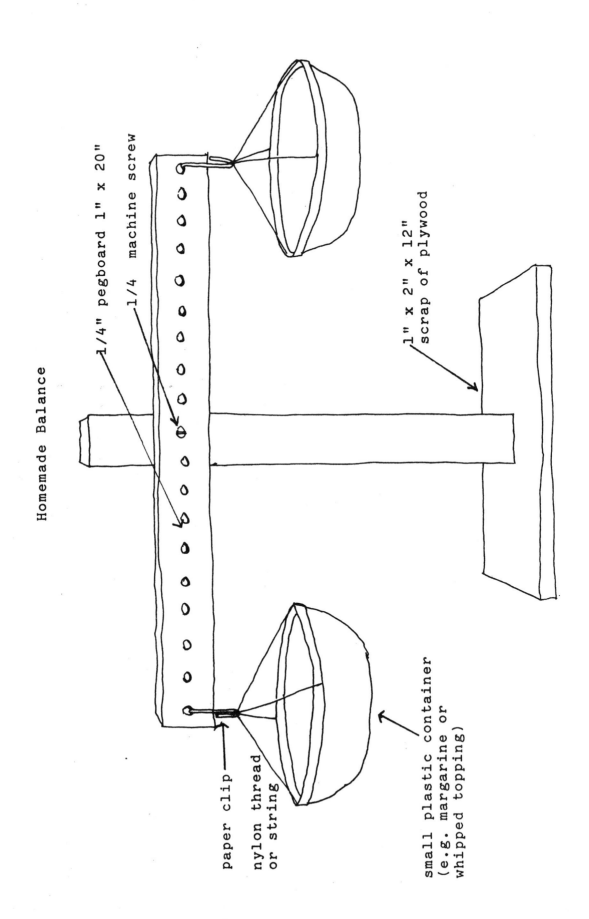

Homemade Balance

1/4" pegboard 1" x 20"

1/4 machine screw

1" x 2" x 12"
scrap of plywood

paper clip

nylon thread
or string

small plastic container
(e.g. margarine or
whipped topping)

LIGHT TABLE

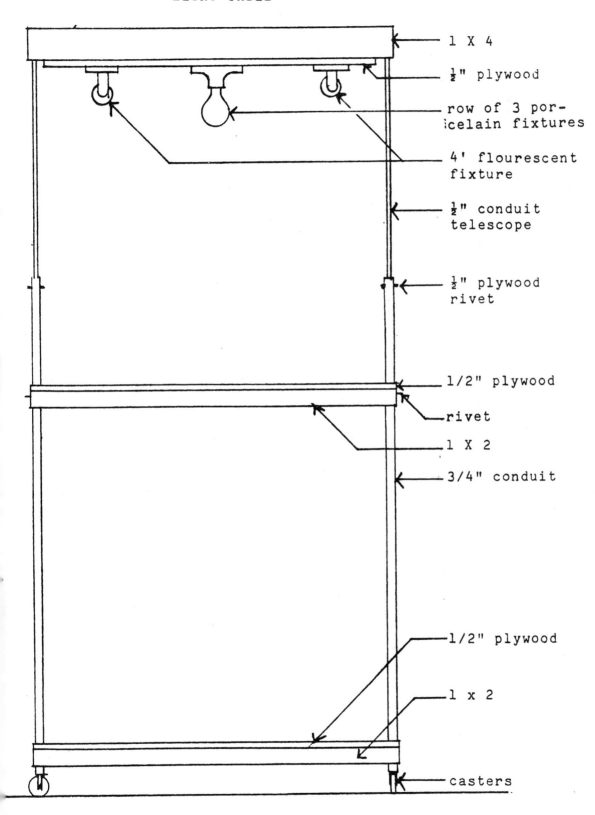

1 X 4

½" plywood

row of 3 por-
celain fixtures

4' flourescent
fixture

½" conduit
telescope

½" plywood
rivet

1/2" plywood

rivet

1 X 2

3/4" conduit

1/2" plywood

1 x 2

casters

Light Table (Front View)

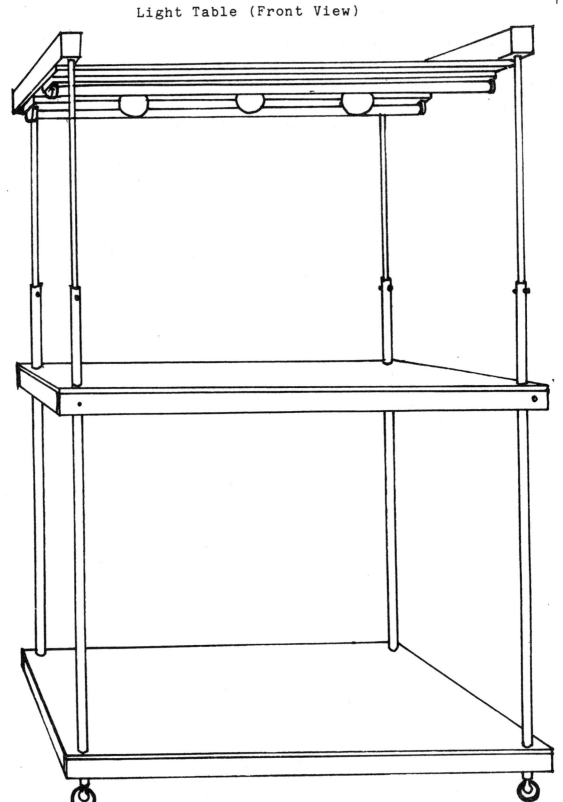

Mealworm Habitat

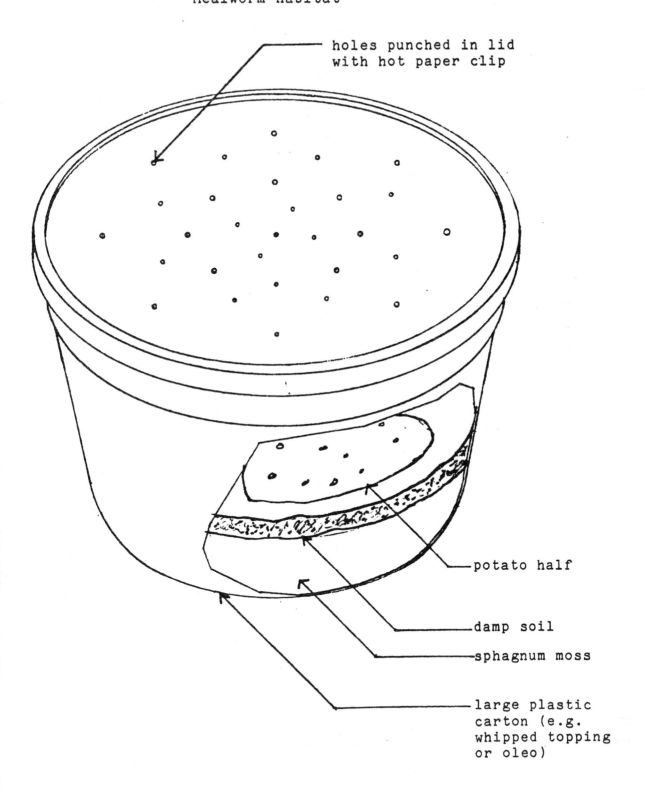

holes punched in lid
with hot paper clip

potato half

damp soil

sphagnum moss

large plastic
carton (e.g.
whipped topping
or oleo)

Plastic Scoop/Funnel

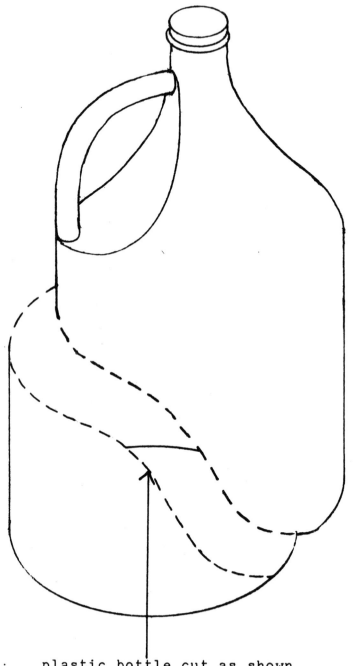

plastic bottle cut as shown
(e.g. bleach, fabric
softener)

Runway to Determine Optimum Temperature Range for Isopods (SCIS Activity--Environments)

Use a sheet of aluminum foil 12" x 22" folded to 6" x 22". Form the sheet into a trough by folding it around the aluminum foil container and folding the ends like a package. Mark divisions at 3" intervals.

Cut 2" x 2" notch for runway Cover cut metal edge with masking tape or binder used on plastic presentation folder.

Gallon cans (paint, coffee, etc.), one filled with ice, one containing light bulb, ceiling receptacle, wire, and plug or socket adopter and extension cord.

Single Snail Habitat

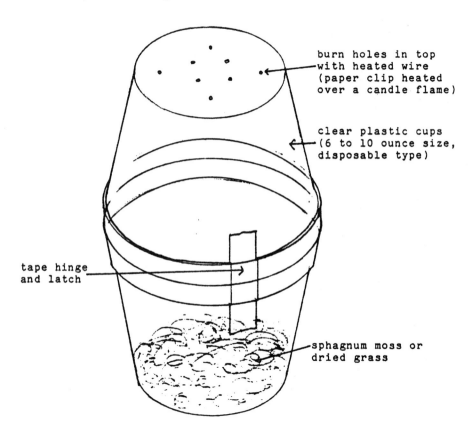

burn holes in top
with heated wire
(paper clip heated
over a candle flame)

clear plastic cups
(6 to 10 ounce size,
disposable type)

tape hinge
and latch

sphagnum moss or
dried grass

Terrarium

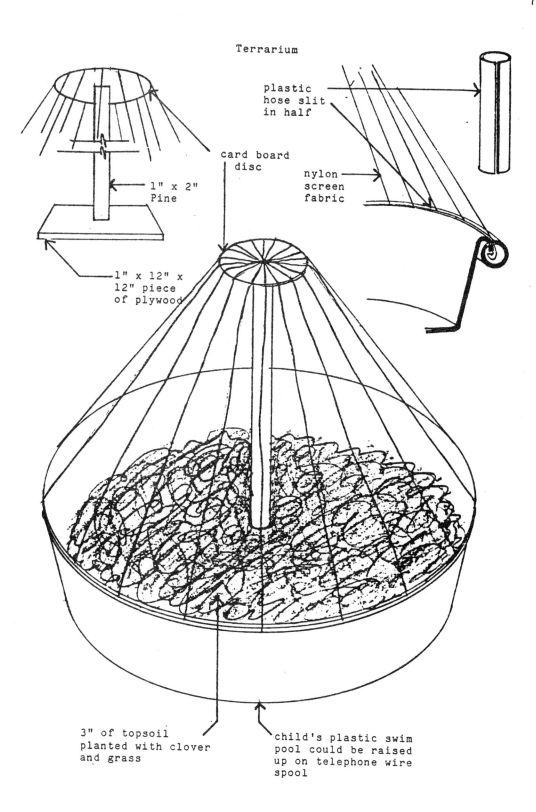

plastic
hose slit
in half

card board
disc

nylon
screen
fabric

1" x 2"
Pine

1" x 12" x
12" piece
of plywood

3" of topsoil
planted with clover
and grass

child's plastic swim
pool could be raised
up on telephone wire
spool

Throw Away Aquarium or Terrarium
(1 to 3 gallon)

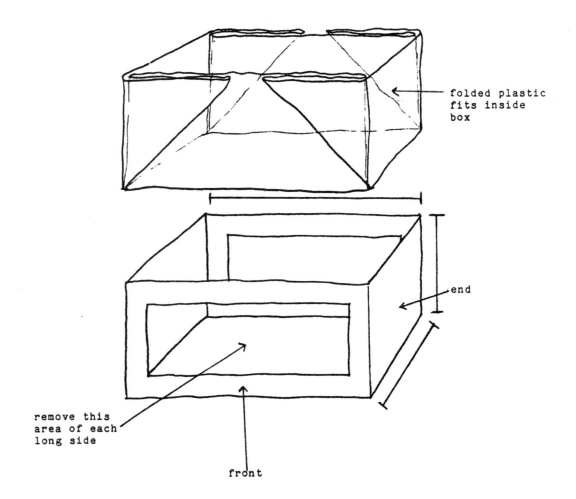

folded plastic
fits inside
box

end

remove this
area of each
long side

front

1. Select a sturdy cardboard carton or corrugated box approximately 12" x 12" x 12" (e.g. nail box from lumberyard).

2. Cut openings as illustrated. (Ends may also be removed if box is sturdy enough.)

3. Paint if desired.

4. Obtain heavy, clear poly sheeting (storm door weight-- approximately 4 mil.)

5. Cut a sheet (a) the length of the box plus the height of two ends and (b) three times the width of the bottom of the box. See diagram. Note: Add one inch to turn over top edge.

6. Fold according to diagram.

7. Place liner in box. Fold edges approximately 1" over top of box. Staple and trim neatly.

Layout for Plastic Liner
4 mil.

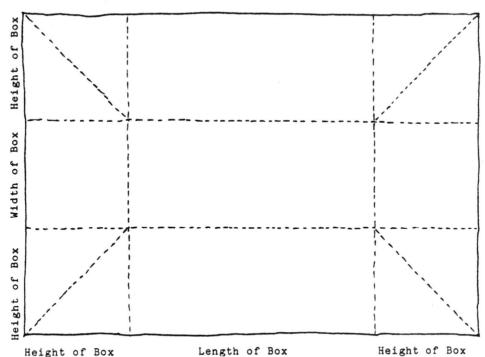

ANNOTATED REFERENCES

1. Comstock, A. B. Handbook of Nature Study. Ithaca,
New York: Cornell Univ. Press, 1963.

     An excellent all-round source of information on
life histories of plants and animals. It contains simple
facts children like to know, is well illustrated, and
provides questions and suggestions about things to look
for.

2. Cornell Science Leaflets. Ithaca, New York: Cornell Univ.
Press, Research Park.

     The leaflets are a superb source of information about
many science activities. Early leaflets are as valuable
as the most recent ones.

3. Palmer, E. L. Fieldbook of Natural History. New York,
New York: McGraw Hill, 1979.

     This book includes 664 pages of drawings and concise
information about rocks, stars, plants and animals. It
is very useful as a quick reference for essential facts.

4. Zim, Herbert, et al. Golden Nature Guides. New York,
New York: Simon & Schuster.

     There are many of these in a useful paperback series.
They are well illustrated, inexpensive and easy to use.
The ones on trees, wild flowers, insects, reptiles and
amphibians, and mammals are especially helpful for primary
grades.

REFERENCES

Abraham, Norman. Biological Science. Englewood Cliffs,
     New Jersey: Prentice-Hall, 1970.

Barkley, T. M. A Manual of the Flowering Plants of Kansas.
     Manhattan, Kansas: The Kansas University Endowment
     Association, 1968.

Bartlett, Ruth. Insect Engineers. New York, New York:
     Morrow & Co. Inc., 1957.

Behavior of Mealworms, Teacher's Guide. New York, New
     York: McGraw-Hill, 1969.

Brandwein, Paul F., et al. Life, A Biological Science.
     New York, New York: Harcourt Brace Jovanovich, 1975.

Brine Shrimp, Teacher's Guide. New York, New York:
     McGraw-Hill, 1969.

Buck, Margaret Waring. In Ponds and Streams. Nashville,
     Tenn.: Abingdon Press, 1955.

Burton, Dr. Maurice & Robert Burton. The International
     Wildlife Encyclopedia. New York, New York: Marshall
     Cavendish Corp., 1970. Vol. 19.

Burton, Dr. Maurice & Robert Burton. The International
     Wildlife Encyclopedia. New York, New York: Marshall
     Cavendish Corp., 1970. Vol. 13.

Burton, Dr. Maurice & Robert Burton. The International
     Wildlife Encyclopedia. New York, New York: Marshall
     Cavendish Corp., 1969. Vol. 6.

Cadbury, B. Bartram. The Community of Living Things in
     Fresh and Salt Water. Mankato, Minnesota: Creative
     Educational Society, 1956.

Conrad, Henry S. How to Know the Mosses and Liverworts.
     Dubuque, Iowa: Wm. C. Brown Co., 1956.

Cook, Christopher, D. K. et al., Water Plants of the
     World. The Hague: Dr. W. Junk, b.v., Publishers,
     1974.

Crayfish, Teacher's Guide. New York, New York: McGraw-Hill, 1968.

deWit, H. C. D. Plants of the World. New York, New York: E. P. Dutton & Co. Inc., 1967.

Eggs and Tadpoles, Teacher's Guide. New York, New York: McGraw-Hill, 1974.

Gaul, Albro. The Pond Book. New York, New York: Coward-McCann, Inc., 1955.

Goudey, Alice. Butterfly Time. New York, New York: Charles Scribners Sons, 1964.

Gray, Alice. Insects. New York, New York: Golden Press, 1965.

Gurdon, J. B. African Clawed Frog. New York, New York: Weatherby Nasco Inc. Taken from Methods in Developmental Biology, 1967.

Hess, Lilo. The Praying Mantis, Insect Cannibal. New York, New York: Charles Scribners Sons, 1971.

Hogner, Dorothy Childs. Moths. New York, New York: Thomas Crowell Co., 1964.

Hutchins, Ross E. The Ant Realm. New York, New York: Dodd, Mead, & Co., 1967.

Hylander, Clarence J. Insects on Parade. New York, New York: Macmillan Co., 1957.

Hylander, Clarence J. Plant Life. New York, New York: Macmillan Co., 1939.

Knott, Robert. et al. Communities. Level 5, Teacher's Guide. Chicago: SCIIS (Rand McNally), 1978.

Knott, Robert, et al. Environments. Teacher's Guide. Chicago: SCIIS (Rand McNally & Co.), 1970.

Lane, Ferdinand. All About the Insect World. New York, New York: Random House, 1954.

Lawson, Chester. Communities. Teacher's Guide. Chicago: SCIS (Rand McNally), 1970.

Lawson, Chester. Environments. Teacher's Guide. Chicago: SCIS (Rand McNally), 1970.

Lawson, Chester. Ecosystems. Teacher's Guide. Chicago: SCIS (Rand Mcnally), 1971.

Lawson, Chester. Life Cycles. Teacher's Guide. Chicago: SCIS (Rand Mcnally), 1970.

Lawson, Chester. Populations. Teacher's Guide. Chicago: SCIS (Rand Mcnally), 1972.

Milne, Lorus & Margery. Living Plants of the World. New York, New York: Random House, 1967.

Moon, Truman J., et al. Modern Biology. New York, New York: Henry Holt & Co., 1951.

Morgan, Alfred. Aquarium Book. New York, New York: Charles Scribners Sons, 1959.

Needham, James & Paul. Fresh Water Biology. San Francisco: Holden-Day, Inc., 1962.

Orlans, F. Barbara. Animal Care from Protozoa to Small Mammals. Reading, Massachusettes: Addison Wesley, 1977.

Peas and Particles. Teacher's Guide. New York, New York: McGraw-Hill, 1974.

Phillips, Mary Geisler. Dragonflies and Damselflies. New York, New York: Thomas Y. Crowell Co., 1960.

Rood, Ronald. Butterflies and Moths. New York, New York: Grosset & Dunlap, 1963.

Schlichting, Harold E. Algae. Austin, Texas: Steck-Vaughn Co., 1971.

Schoenknecht, Charles A. Ants. Chicago: Follett Pub. Co., 1961.

Sculthorpe, C. D. The Biology of Aquatic Vascular Plants. New York, New York: St. Martin's Press, 1967.

Simon, Hilda. Insect Masquerades. New York, New York: Viking Press, 1969.

Street, Philip. Animal Reproduction. New York, New York: Taplinger Publishing Co. Inc., 1974.

Subarsky, Zachariah, et al. <u>Living Things in Field and Classroom</u>. Minneapolis: University of Minnesota, 1967.

Zim. Herbert S. & Clarence Cottam. <u>Insects</u>. New York, New York: Golden Press, 1964.

Zim, Herbert. <u>Plants</u>. New York, New York: Harcourt, Brace & World, Inc., 1947.

Zim, Herbert, & Hobart M. Smith. <u>Reptiles & Amphibians</u>. New York, New York: Simon & Schuster (Golden Nature Guide), 1953.

APPENDICES

Appendix A

BIOLOGICAL HAZARD

CAUTION: DO NOT RELEASE NON-NATIVE LIVING MATERIAL INTO
           YOUR LOCAL ENVIRONMENT

If this live material cannot be maintained with
security in your classroom or laboratory, it should be
destroyed.   Instruction for destroying live material
follows.

All organisms can be terminated or anesthetized
by low temperatures: plants and invertebrates by
freezing; cold blooded vertebrates anesthetized by cold
and preserved in 10% formalin; warm blooded vertebrates
by prolonged anesthesia with ether in an airtight container; final disposal by incineration.

If released, any organism not native to your local
environment has the potential of destroying the ecological
balance.   This applies to everything from algae and daphnia
to snails and frogs.

*Reprinted by permission fron NASCO

Appendix B

BIOLOGICAL SUPPLIERS
(Living Material and Equipment)

The Butterfly Breeding Farm
275 Colwick Road
Rochester, New York 14624

Cambasco Scientific Co.
342 Western Ave.
Boston, Mass.

Carolina Biological Supply Co.
Burlington, N.C. 27215

Central Scientific Co.
2600 S. Kostner Ave.
Chicago, Ill. 60623

Everglades Aquatic Nurseries, Inc.
P.O. Box 587-706 Plaza Place
Tampa, Fl. 33601

Giant Ant Farm
Dept. 35
1238 N. Highland Ave.
Hollywood, Cal. 90038

Insect Control & Research, Inc.
1330 Dillon Heights Ave.
Baltimore, Md. 21228

Macmillian Science Co.
8200 S. Hoyne Ave.
Chicago, Ill. 60620

Mogul-Ed.
P.O. Box 482
Oshkosh, Wis. 54901

NASCO
Fot Atkinson, Wis. 53538
    or
P.O. Box 3837
1524 Princeton Ave.
Modesto, CA 95352

Rand McNally & Co.
P.O. Box 7600
Chicago, Ill. 60680

Sargent-Welch Scientific Co.
7300 W. Linder Ave.
Skokie, Ill. 60076

Selective Educ. Equipment, Inc
Three Bridge Street
Newton, Mass. 02195

Stansi Scientific Div.
Fisher Scientific Co.
1237 Honore St.
Chicago, Ill. 60622

Sure-Live Mealworm Co.
P.O. Box 827
Paramount, CA 90723

Ward's Natural Science Est.
Box 1712
Rochester, New Jersey 14603

COMPARISON OF AMERICAN AND METRIC UNITS OF MEASUREMENT

A Conversion Method

Linear (length) Relationships

10mm = 1cm	10dm = 1m
10cm = 1dm	1000m = 1km

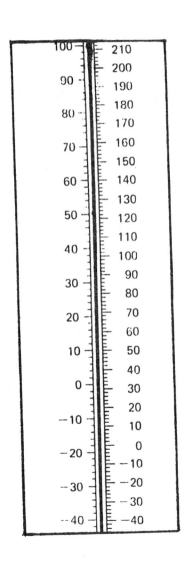

Temperature Relationships

°C	°F	Conditions
0	32	Freezing point
22	72	Comfortable room temp.
37	98.6	Normal body temperature
40	105	Dangerous fever level
100	212	Boiling water

LIVING MATERIALS FOOD CHART

Organisms listed across the top are consumers of the materials listed at the left.

Animal and Terrarium Plant Food	Ants	Aphids	Brine Shrimp	Butterflies	Chameleons	Cockroaches	Crayfish	Crickets	Daphnia	Damselfly	D.nymph	Frogs	Fruit Fly	Guppies	Hermit Crab	Isopods	Land Snails	Mealworms	Moths	Pond Snails	Praying Mantis	Salamander	Tadpoles	Toads	Turtle	Plants
Algae			●						●						●					●			●			
Brine Shrimp Eggs														●												
Bread of Apple																										
Crickets and Cockroaches					●							●									●	●		●		
Cabbage or Lettuce						●		●									●								●	
Daphnia											●			●												
Flowers or Leaves that animal is found on				●															●							
Tetrament (or equivalent)														●												
Fruits (banana)													●													
Earthworms					●		●					●								●	●		●			

"Bottled" noted in the Tadpoles column.

*Reprinted by permission of NASCO.

LIVING MATERIALS FOOD CHART (Continued)

Organisms listed across the top are consumers of the materials listed at the left.

Animal and Terrarium Plant Foods	Ants	Aphids	Brine Shrimp	Butterflies	Chameleons	Cockroaches	Crayfish	Crickets	Daphnia	Damselfly	Nymph	Frogs	Fruit Fly	Guppies	Hermit Crab	Isopods	Land Snails	Mealworms	Moths	Pond Snails	Praying Mantis	Salamander	Tadpoles	Toads	Turtle	Plants
Raw Meats (Liver)							●																		●	
Mag Amp Fertilizer																										●
Dogfood, Roller Meal or Oats						●		●										●								
Mealworms					●		●					●			●						●	●		●		
Dead Leaves					●																					
Sowbugs (Isopods)																●										
Potatoe																		●								
Nasco Food Pellets						●	●	●															●	●	●	
Prepared culture medium		●											●													
Pea Plant or equivalent																										
Redworms					●		●					●										●		●		
Yeast of equivalent			●																							
Aquaria Plants																				●						
Fruit Flies and Mosquitoes										● (larva)																

by permission of NASCO.

Appendix E

TEMPORARY CARE FOR NEW ANIMAL ARRIVALS

What To Do With Them Until Class Time!

These instructions are intended for temporary help on
arrival only. Please consult your SCIS Teachers Guides
for the necessary instructions on preparation of environments, class use and long term maintenance.

Aphids: Open capsule by removing tape around middle.
Bottom half holds a pellet with a pea seedling and aphids.
Check inside of top for stray aphids which may be care-
fully brushed onto seedling with camels hair brush. If
pellet seems dry add enough water to set thoroughly.
Place seedling, in cup in COOL place where it will receive
some light, but NOT direct sunlight.

Chameleons: Place a crumpled paper towel in terrarium.
Break seal of shipping container and QUICKLY empty
chameleons into terrarium and close lid. Spray water on
inside walls and vegetation daily. Chameleons will not
drink from dishes. Moisture licked from walls and leaves
is their only source of water. They will need no feeding
until class time.

Chlamydomonas: Loosen cap immediately and place where it
will receive good light without excessive heat.

Crickets: Crickets are shipped in a box with crumpled
paper. They dislike overcrowding and should be transferred
to terraria as soon as possible. To empty box, slit tape
and raise the two upper flaps. Turn upside down over
terrarium, open lower flaps and shake box. Paper and
crickets will fall out. Some crickets may cling to box.
Brush them into terrarium and close lid.

Damselfly Larvae: Open jar immediately. Hungry damselfly
larvae will attack each other, therefore we suggest that
they be placed in SEPARATE containers of aged room temperature tap water as soon as possible. Consult your "Populations" Teachers Guide and appendix.

Daphnia: Open cap to admit air. Shipping water contains
food supply. Leave in shipping water until use.

Frog Eggs: Open container immediately. Pour off shipping water and replace with spring water or aged tap water. Place in aquarium as soon as possible. Keep at room temperature and out of sunlight.

Fruit Flies: Keep fly cultures at room temperature, out of direct sunlight. Add a few drops of water if culture dries out. Keep food vials in refrigerator. It is characteristic of this food that it will turn black with use and age. This is due to the fruit content of the medium, and does NOT indicate a mold.

Guppies: Float unopened bag in container of aged tap water for about 10 to 15 minutes to equalize the temperature. When temperatures are equal (test with finger of clean soap free hand) pour contents of bag through a dip net. Transfer guppies from net to container of aged tap water. Discard shipping water.

Hydra: Open cap to admit air. Store in cool place until use.

Isopods: (Sowbugs) Sowbugs are shipped in a container with damp paper and a "breathing" cap to provide both moisture and air. Place them in suitable terraria, as described in your SCIS Teachers Guide, as soon as possible.

Mealworm Beetles: Mealworm beetles are shipped in a container with a "breathing" cap to provide air. They need no special care, but should be used as soon as possible, as they have a rather short life span. If kept in a bran filled container as described in the appendix of your SCIS "Environments" Teachers Guide the beetles will lay eggs and start another life cycle.

Mealworms: Store in a cool place 45 to 65 degrees Fahrenheit. Mealworms may be refrigerated as long as several weeks. If left at room temperature they will soon pupate.

Pond Snails: If snails are to be held for more than a few hours before transfer to aquaria, place bag in cup or similar upright container to prevent tipping, and open top of bag.

Snails: Land snails are active only in a humid environment. Place them in a terrarium, as described in the appendix of your SCIS Teachers Guide, as soon as possible.

Sowbugs: (Isopods) Sowbugs are shipped in a container with damp paper and a "breathing" cap to provide both moisture and air. Place them in suitable terraria, as described in your SCIS Teachers Guide, as soon as possible.

*Reprinted with permission from NASCO.

APPENDIX F

TEMPORARY CARE FOR NEW PLANT ARRIVALS

What To Do With Them Until Class Time!

These instructions are intended for temporary help on arrival only. Please consult your SCIS Teachers' Guides for the necessary instructions on preparation of environments, class use and long term maintenance.

Algae: (Chlamydomonas) Loosen cap immediately and place where it will receive good light without excessive heat.

Anacharis: (Elodea) Keep wet. Cover completely with aged tap water. Place where it will receive some light, but NOT direct sunlight.

Vallisneria   (Eelgrass) Keep wet. Cover completely with aged tap water. Keep in bright spot, but NOT in direct sunlight.

Wolffia: (Duckweed) Loosen cap. May be kept in jar until transfer to aged tap water. Keep in bright spot, but NOT in direct sunlight.

NEW DIRECTIONS IN ETHNIC STUDIES: MINORITIES IN AMERICA by David
     Claerbaut, Editor   Perfect Bound   LC# 80-69327
     ISBN 0-86548-025-7 $9.95
COLLECTING, CULTURING, AND CARING FOR LIVING MATERIALS: GUIDE FOR
     TEACHER, STUDENT AND HOBBYIST by William E. Claflin   Perfect
     Bound   LC# 80-69329   ISBN 0-86548-026-5 $8.50
TEACHING ABOUT THE OTHER AMERICANS: MINORITIES IN UNITED STATES
     HISTORY by Ann Curry   Perfect Bound   LC# 80-69120
     ISBN 0-86548-028-1 $8.95
MULTICULTURAL TRANSACTIONS: A WORKBOOK FOCUSING ON COMMUNICATION
     BETWEEN GROUPS by James S. DeLo and William A. Green   Perfect
     Bound   LC# 80-69328   ISBN 0-86548-030-3 $11.50
LEARNING TO TEACH by Richard B. Dierenfield   Perfect Bound
     LC# 80-69119   ISBN 0-86548-031-1 $10.95
LEARNING TO THINK--TO LEARN by M. Ann Dirkes   Perfect Bound
     LC# 80-65613   ISBN 0-86548-032-X $11.50
PLAY IN PRESCHOOL MAINSTREAMED AND HANDICAPPED SETTINGS by Anne Cairns
     Federlein   Perfect Bound   LC# 80-65612   ISBN 0-86548-035-4
     $10.50
THE NATURE OF LEADERSHIP FOR HISPANICS AND OTHER MINORITIES by
     Ernest Yutze Flores   Perfect Bound   LC# 80-69239
     ISBN 0-86548-036-2 $10.95
THE MINI-GUIDE TO LEADERSHIP by Ernest Yutze Flores   Perfect Bound
     LC# 80-83627   ISBN 0-86548-037-0 $5.50
THOUGHTS, TROUBLES AND THINGS ABOUT READING FROM THE CRADLE THROUGH
     GRADE THREE by Carolyn T. Gracenin   Perfect Bound
     LC# 80-65611   ISBN 0-86548-038-9 $14.95
BETWEEN TWO CULTURES: THE VIETNAMESE IN AMERICA by Alan B. Henkin and
     Liem Thanh Nguyen   Perfect Bound   LC# 80-69333
     ISBN 0-86548-039-7 $7.95
PERSONALITY CHARACTERISTICS AND DISCIPLINARY ATTITUDES OF CHILD-
     ABUSING MOTHERS by Alan L. Evans   Perfect Bound   LC# 80-69240
     ISBN 0-86548-033-8 $11.95
PARENTAL EXPECTATIONS AND ATTITUDES ABOUT CHILDREARING IN HIGH RISK
     VS. LOW RISK CHILD ABUSING FAMILIES by Gary C. Rosenblatt
     Perfect Bound   LC# 79-93294   ISBN 0-86548-020-6 $10.00
CHILD ABUSE AS VIEWED BY SUBURBAN ELEMENTARY SCHOOL TEACHERS by David
     A. Pelcovitz   Perfect Bound   LC# 79-93295   ISBN 0-86548-019-2
     $10.00
PHYSICAL CHILD ABUSE: AN EXPANDED ANALYSIS by James R. Seaberg
     Perfect Bound   LC# 79-93293   ISBN 0-86548-021-4 $10.00
THE DISPOSITION OF REPORTED CHILD ABUSE by Marc F. Maden   Perfect
     Bound   LC# 79-93296   ISBN 0-86548-016-8 $10.00
EDUCATIONAL AND PSYCHOLOGICAL PROBLEMS OF ABUSED CHILDREN by James
     Christiansen   Perfect Bound   LC# 79-93303   ISBN 0-86548-003-6
     $10.00
DEPENDENCY, FRUSTRATION TOLERANCE, AND IMPULSE CONTROL IN CHILD ABUSERS
     by Don Kertzman   Perfect Bound   LC# 79-93297   ISBN 86548-015-X
     $10.00
SUCCESSFUL STUDENT TEACHING: A HANDBOOK FOR ELEMENTARY AND SECONDARY
     STUDENT TEACHERS by Fillmer Hevener, Jr.   Perfect Bound
     LC# 80-69332   ISBN 0-86548-040-0 $8.95
BLACK COMMUNICATION IN WHITE SOCIETY by Roy Cogdell and Sybil Wilson
     Perfect Bound   LC# 79-93302   ISBN 0-86548-004-4 $13.00

SCHOOL VANDALISM: CAUSE AND CURE by Robert Bruce Williams and Joseph
    L. Venturini   Perfect Bound   LC# 80-69230   ISBN 0-86548-060-5
    $9.50
LEADERS, LEADING, AND LEADERSHIP by Harold W. Boles   Perfect Bound
    LC# 80-65616   ISBN 0-86548-023-0 $14.95
LEGAL OUTLOOK: A MESSAGE TO COLLEGE AND UNIVERSITY PEOPLE by Ulysses
    V. Spiva   Perfect Bound   LC# 80-69232   ISBN 0-86548-057-5
    $9.95
THE NAKED CHILD THE LONG RANGE EFFECTS OF FAMILY AND SOCIAL NUDITY
    by Dennis Craig Smith   Perfect Bound   LC# 80-69234
    ISBN 0-86548-056-7 $7.95
SIGNIFICANT INFLUENCE PEOPLE: A SIP OF DISCIPLINE AND ENCOURAGEMENT
    by Joseph C. Rotter, Johnnie McFadden and Gary D. Kannenberg
    Perfect Bound   LC# 80-69233   ISBN 0-86548-055-9 $8.95
LET'S HAVE FUN WITH ENGLISH by Ruth Rackmill   Perfect Bound
    LC# 80-68407   ISBN 0-86548-061-3 $6.95
CHILDREN'S PERCEPTIONS OF ELDERLY PERSONS by Lillian A. Phenice
    Perfect Bound   LC# 80-65604   ISBN 0-86548-054-0 $10.50
URBAN EDUCATION: AN ANNOTATED BIBLIOGRAPHY by Arnold G. Parks
    Perfect Bound   LC# 80-69234   ISBN 0-86548-053-2 $9.50
DYNAMICS OF CLASSROOM STRUCTURE by Charles J. Nier   Perfect Bound
    LC# 80-69330   ISBN 0-86548-052-4 $11.50
SOCIOLOGY IN BONDAGE: AN INTRODUCTION TO GRADUATE STUDY by Harold A.
    Nelson   Perfect Bound   LC# 80-65605   ISBN 0-86548-051-6 $9.95
BEYOND THE OPEN CLASSROOM: TOWARD INFORMAL EDUCATION by Lorraine L.
    Morgan, Vivien C. Richman and Ann Baldwin Taylor   Perfect Bound
    LC# 80-69235   ISBN 0-86548-050-8 $9.50
INTRODUCTORY SOCIOLOGY: LECTURES, READINGS AND EXERCISES by Gordon D.
    Morgan   Perfect Bound   LC# 80-65606   ISBN 0-86548-049-4
    $10.50
THE STUDENT TEACHER ON THE FIRING LINE by D. Eugene Meyer   Perfect
    Bound   LC# 80-69236   ISBN 0-86548-048-6 $11.95
VALUES ORIENTATION IN SCHOOL by Johnnie McFadden and Joseph C. Rotter
    Perfect Bound   LC# 80-69238   ISBN 0-86548-045-1 $4.50
MOVEMENT THEMES: TOPICS FOR EARLY CHILDHOOD LEARNING THROUGH CREATIVE
    MOVEMENT by Barbara Stewart Jones   Perfect Bound   LC# 80-65608
    ISBN 0-86548-042-7 $8.50
FROM BIRTH TO TWELVE: HOW TO BE A SUCCESSFUL PARENT TO INFANTS AND
    CHILDREN by Gary D. Kannenberg   Perfect Bound   LC# 80-69331
    ISBN 0-86548-043-5 $7.95